THE NELSON
PROFICIENCY
WORKBOOK

Susan Morris, Alan Stanton

REVISED EDITION

Nelson

Nelson English Language Teaching
100 Avenue Road
London NW3 3HF

An International Thomson Publishing Company

London • Bonn • Boston • Madrid • Melbourne • Mexico City
• New York • Paris • Singapore • Tokyo

© Susan Morris, Alan Stanton 1990, 1994

Original edition first published by Nelson ELT 1990
This edition first published by Nelson ELT 1994, a division of
Thomas Nelson and Sons Ltd

ISBN 0–17–556888–X

NPN 9 8 7 6 5 4 3 2

Printed in Hong Kong.

Contents

Introduction

The Nelson Proficiency Workbook forms part of the Nelson Proficiency Course, which has as its main components a Students' Book and two cassettes. There is also a Teacher's Book. The Workbook provides additional practice material in grammar and vocabulary. It can be used in the classroom to provide supplementary exercises on particular areas of language study. You can also use it when studying at home and you can check your work against the Answer Key given at the back of the book.

The Workbook is divided into twelve sections. Each section contains exercises on a special area of grammar or vocabulary instead of corresponding exactly with the contents of individual units in the Students' Book.

The best way to approach the Workbook, therefore, is to study the Contents list. Choose an area in which you are not yet fully confident and turn to that section to do the exercises. It is a good idea to do all the exercises in a section, although you may find some exercises at the beginning quite easy. It is not necessary to go through the sections in the order in which they appear in the Workbook.

Clear, simple instructions are given for each exercise. In many cases, there is an example at the beginning of the exercise to show you the sort of answer you should give. When you have finished the exercise, turn to the answers at the back of the book and find out if you were right. Use the Workbook regularly in order to check your own progress.

Articles, Quantifiers and their Compounds

A *Complete the gaps with **a** or **an**.*

Frank Crawford is ...an....... (1) American citizen. He is also ......an..... (2) F.B.I. agent (and has ......an... (3) ID card to prove it) whose qualifications include ....an. (4) M.A. and ....a..... (5) Ph.D. – and he has ......an.... (6) I.Q. of 160. Because his father was ......an... (7) M.P. in England and his mother, ...an..... (8) Italian, worked as ......a...... (9) G.P. there, Frank often sees things from .....a....... (10) European perspective. He strongly supports the idea of ......a...... (11) united Europe. He was recently in London for ....a..... (12) one-day conference on organised crime, and he gave a speech which lasted ......an..... (13) hour. (You can get a copy of his speech by sending ....an.. (14) s.a.e. to the address below). When in London he always stays at ......a...... (15) hotel in Holland Park, where he always eats ....an... (16) onion for breakfast. When Frank inherited a fortune from ......an..... (17) uncle recently, he used it to found ....a..... (18) university and buy ......an... (19) X-ray machine for ....a.... (20) hospital.

B *Some of the following sentences are correct as they stand; others need **the** added to them. Indicate where **the** is needed.*

1 Martina is learning to play *the* violin.

2 Jennifer is learning to play chess. √

3 'Is this *the* Oxford road?' said the lorry driver.

4 John works in a shop in Oxford Street. √

5 The book consists of quotations from great philosophers. √

6 We reached our destination at sunset. √

7 Terry spent *the* summer climbing in *the* Alps.

8 After they had completed their work in *the* prison, the bricklayers and plasterers moved to another site.

9 Mr Watt refused even to visit *the* home his relatives wanted to put him in.

10 History was his favourite subject at school. √

5

C *Complete the sentences with* **some** *or* **any**. *(In some sentences it is possible to use either.)*

1 You can have ......any... box you like – they're all the same.

2 I can meet you ...any.... afternoon next week. Which one suits you best?

3 Martin has .....some.. information about the conference.

4 ...Any.... person who trespasses on this land will be reported to the police.

5 The director didn't like .....any.. of the clauses in his new contract.

6 ....Some... of the points on the agenda were not discussed because there wasn't enough time.

7 They are very anxious to sell the house and will probably accept ...any... offer you make.

8 Have you .....any... idea how long this job will take?

9 ...Any.. of these paths will take you back to the village – so you can't possibly get lost.

10 The manager didn't like .....any.... of the things that were said at the meeting.

D *(Follow the instructions in Exercise* **C**)

1 'Who was it on the phone?'
'It was just ......some.. man trying to sell us a new kitchen.'

2 'Peter's friend owes him £5,000 and has left the country!'
'...Some... friend!'

3 The first national conference was attended by ....some... six hundred delegates.

4 Goods can be collected at .....any.... time.

5 You can use ......any..... currency to purchase your ticket.

6 The car won't go ....any..... faster.

7 The job is too difficult to be done by ....any.... one person.

8 It is a shame that ....any.. animal should suffer in that way.

9 ...Some..... of the performers will arrive two days later than planned.

10 After the hurricane struck the town, there was ....some... looting.

E *Complete the sentences with one of the following:* **anyone, anything, any time, any more, anywhere, nothing, somehow, someone, something, sometime, some time, somewhere**.

1 Your driver will take you ......*anywhere*...... you wish to go on the island.

2 Come up and see me ......*sometime*, *any time*.

3 'Is there ....*anything*, *any more*.... you want to tell me, George?' said Elizabeth.

4 You can put the books ......*anywhere*.... you like.

5 Despite the excellent qualifications and experience of several candidates, we couldn't find ....*anyone*.......... who we thought would be the right man for the job.

6 Hurry up! We haven't ....*any time*.... to waste.

7 I would really like to return to that island ......*somehow*, *sometime*

8 ...., nothing seemed to go smoothly, from the time we started rehearsing to the last night.

9 The storm prevented us from continuing the climb for quite ....*any more*....

10 The bandits are believed to be hiding .... in the hills.

F *(Follow the instructions in Exercise* **E***)*

1 *Someone*............ has cut the telephone wires.

2 *Nothing*.......... I said would cheer him up.

3 These donkeys cannot carry ....*any more* goods.

4 *Anything*......... you say will be taken down and may be used in evidence against you.

5 ....*Any more*... fares?

6 I am afraid it will be ....*some time*.... before Diana can leave hospital.

7 In his present serious condition, I think that the doctors would be willing to try ......*anything*.. that might improve matters.

8 Sandra is really ambitious and there is ....*nothing*......... she wouldn't do to get into the national team.

9 If there was ....*anything*......... Maurice didn't know about Greek art, we never discovered what it was.

10 Would you like ......*someone*.... to help you carry your shopping to your car?

G *Tick the columns to show which combinations of words are acceptable. If you think it is acceptable to say* **many eggs**, *then tick that column. If you think it is unacceptable, leave the column blank. The first line has already been done for you.*

	many 1	these 2	most 3	my 4	a little 5	the 6	a 7	a lot of 8	a few 9	both 10
information		✓	✓	✓	✓	✓		✓	✓	✓
eggs	✓		✓	✓	✓	✓		✓	✓	✓
luggage			✓	✓	✓	✓		✓	✓	✓
questions	✓	✓	✓	✓		✓		✓	✓	✓
furniture			✓	✓	✓	✓		✓		✓
enquiries	✓	✓	✓	✓		✓		✓	✓	✓
money			✓	✓	✓	✓		✓		
advice			✓	✓	✓	✓		✓		
news			✓	✓	✓	✓		✓		✓
progress			✓	✓	✓	✓		✓		

H *(Follow the instructions in Exercise* **G***)*

	plenty of 1	enough 2	few 3	a little 4	some 5	all 6	every 7	ten 8	those 9	less 10
cows	✓	✓	✓		✓	✓		✓	✓	
clothes										
hair										
laugh										
experience										
laughter										
police										
intelligence										
strength										
book										

Verb Tenses (active and passive)

A *Put the verbs in the correct form, using either the simple present or present continuous.*

1 The line (be) very bad. I can't hear what you (say).

2 'I (look) for a builder to do some work on my house. You (know) anyone who (be) suitable and (be) available at the moment?'
'Afraid not. Everyone I (know) (be) up to their eyes in work repairing the damage caused by the gales.'

3 Rob, I (try) to concentrate, but it (be) very difficult. The children (make) too much noise. You (think) you could take them out for an hour or so?

4 I (believe) Tom (be) the person who (try) to sell his house. He (want) to move out of the city.

5 Jeremy, you (be) rather foolish in refusing to speak. Everyone (get) rather fed up with your behaviour.

6 Anna (make) a lot of progress learning Russian mainly because she now (spend) two hours a day studying.

7 I always (tidy up) my desk before I (leave) work.

8 Tony always (criticise) his family – they never (do) the right thing as far as he is concerned.

9 Tell me all about it. I (die) to hear all the latest news.

10 Oil (leak) from a petrol tanker onto the motorway, so the police (close) off the section between Junctions 5 and 6.

B *Complete the following sentences by putting the verb in either a future or present form as appropriate.*

1 Stephen not (be) happy until he (be promoted) to the Chief Accountant's job.

2 When the sun (set) this evening, the sky for miles around (be suffused) with a rosy glow.

3 I (ring) my parents the moment I (get) my exam results.

4 Many industrialists (predict) a major increase in trade when the new road network (come) into operation.

5 By the time Anthony (finish) work on the design project, he (be) exhausted.

6 The Opposition (be) ready and waiting to exploit any sign of disunity in the government as soon as it (appear).

7 If you (have) no objections, we (go ahead) with the project as planned.

8 What (be) the state of the planet when we (reach) the year 2100?

9 Once we (get) a reply from the ministry, we (be able) to confirm our intentions.

10 Before Alice (sign) the contract, she (need) to ensure that every detail (be) correct.

Verb Tenses (active and passive)

C *Put the verbs in brackets in the correct form, using either the present perfect or simple past tense as appropriate.*

1 This is the first time I (visit) Hungary.

2 On my visit to the school, I (be) pleased to see that many students (know) how to handle computers.

3 This is the best steak I ever (taste).

4 Sally (live) and (work) in Paris for several years now.

5 For five years from 1980 to 1985, Tom (live) in Madrid.

6 I already (read) 200 pages and so I expect to finish the book by the weekend.

7 Yesterday I (work) for six hours and (complete) two reports.

8 Jane is only six and already she (pass) two piano exams.

9 Although I (know) Sarah and Frank for many years now, I never (understand) what (attract) them to each other.

10 I never (be) so pleased as when I (hear) Anna had recovered from her illness.

D *Put the verbs in brackets in the correct form, using either the past continuous or simple past tense.*

1 Jane (live) in France when she (meet) the man who later (become) her husband.

2 When Terry (hear) the job he (want) (be) his, he immediately (invite) his colleagues out for a celebration.

3 When the liner (hit) the iceberg, most of the passengers (have) dinner.

4 I (can) not accept Richard's invitation to dinner because I (go) to the theatre that night.

5 Try as we might, it (be) impossible to manoeuvre our sailing boat out of the harbour. The wind (blow) too hard.

6 It (be) a horrible day. Everything that (can) go wrong (do). The children (get) up late. The cat (be) sick. The car not (start). I just (want) to give up.

7 The clock just (strike) twelve when Cinderella (come) back from the ball.

8 The manager not (be) available. He (travel) to a meeting in Edinburgh.

9 Annabel not (ride) in the horse trials. No one (be) surprised when she later (announce) she (expect) a baby.

10 It (be) a fabulous day. The sun (shine), the birds (sing), the countryside (look) lovely.

E *Put the verbs in brackets in the correct form, using the present perfect simple or continuous as appropriate.*

1 I (love) Tim all my life.

2 I always (want) to travel around the world.

3 How many times I (be asked) why I live in the country?

4 Doctor, I (have) trouble with my hands for months. What's wrong?

5 Colin (have) bad headaches for two months now. They suspect a brain tumour.

6 You don't know what *vir* means! How long you (study) Latin?

7 I (try) to get you on the phone for over a week. Where you (be)?

8 'Janet's looking very fit.'
'Yes, she (go) to exercise classes.'

9 Who (take) my pen?

10 'Who (sleep) in my bed?' Jane asked, looking at the rumpled sheets.

F *Put the verbs in brackets in the correct form, using the past perfect or simple past tense as appropriate. Use the continuous forms if necessary.*

1 Jake (graduate) in 1987 and (spend) two years applying for jobs before he (be offered) the one he (want).

2 Tom (look) for the right person to be his wife for five years before he (meet) and (fall) in love with Sally.

3 If I (know) what to do, everything would have been all right. As it (be), everything (go) wrong.

4 Mary (have) a nervous breakdown last year. No one (be) surprised. She (work) much too hard for months.

5 The garden (look) absolutely lovely last year, mainly because of the hard work we (put in) the previous autumn.

6 Stories about the two politicians and their liaison (circulate) for many months before any statement (be made).

7 John (receive) treatment for two years before he finally (be told) he (be cured).

8 Before she (begin) her university course, Lesley (read) all the books on the first year reading list.

9 'Why you not (go) to see the film at the Odeon last week. I (think) you (like) Paul Newman.'
'Because I already (see) it. I (go) when it (be) on in London.'

10 'Why (be) you not at the meeting?'
'I not (be told) about it.'

Verb Tenses (active and passive)

G *Add the appropriate question tag to the following sentences.*

EXAMPLE: I suppose you wish I would come and see you whenever I can, *don't you?*

1 You used to be in the army, ...?

2 I'm going to play Hamlet in our next production, ...?

3 They ought to be here by now, ...?

4 She must have known what was happening, ...?

5 You'd better get the work finished by Tuesday, ...?

6 I think you'd rather do it by yourself, ...?

7 It might have been a ghost, ...?

8 It couldn't have been done by an animal, ...?

9 I'm not sure that that's the right answer, ...?

10 It's a pity that Sheila didn't know about it, ...?

11 It will be the minister who decides what must be done if people refuse to pay, ...?

12 He wouldn't have been arrested if the policeman hadn't seen through his disguise, ...?

13 Let's go to the beach, ...?

14 Stop that noise, ...!

15 I don't think he could have known what was going to happen, ...?

16 Don't spend all your money at once, ...?

17 They didn't, ...?

18 Do have another cucumber sandwich, ...?

19 Nobody will believe that you are really Roger Tichborne, ...?

20 There was nothing we could do about the decisions he made, ...?

H *Rewrite these sentences using a passive verb. Do not use* **by**.

EXAMPLE: They asked everyone to make a statement.
          Everyone was asked to make a statement.

1 You must check all the pipes for leaks.

2 They announced an increased dividend.

3 We will investigate the complaint thoroughly.

4 No one knew the place where the treasure was buried.

5 Somebody might have informed the police.

6 No one had noticed the cracks in the side of the fuselage.

7 No one would ever have known the truth if we hadn't found the diary.

8 They would have arrested him if they had realised his true identity.

9 Did they discuss anything important?

10 On the site you have to wear a safety helmet.

I *Rewrite these sentences using a passive verb. Include* **by** *in your sentence.*

1 Guards patrol these premises every day.

2 The doctor is studying the X-rays.

3 The mechanic will repair the car tomorrow.

4 Martin, our new gardener, has planted seven apple trees.

5 The burglars took nothing of any real value.

6 Robbers had opened the tomb long before archaeologists found it.

7 The smugglers were transferring the drugs from one car to another when the police arrived.

8 A famous architect is going to design Lord Fauntleroy's country-house.

9 Motorists convicted of speeding must pay a minimum fine of £100.

10 The museum might lose its annual government subsidy.

J *Rewrite the following sentences using the passive. Think carefully about whether or not the agent needs to be referred to and whether every verb in each sentence needs to be passive.*

1 Someone told me that the best way to get marks off my trousers was to have them cleaned.

2 It was a shock for everyone when they announced the news of the disaster.

3 It was Newton who formulated the law of gravity.

4 Judith left the house under cover of darkness so that no one would see her.

5 An aide to the minister revealed details of the secret meeting with the representatives of the terrorist organisation.

6 They say that James is the most gifted mathematician the department has ever produced.

7 If they had found the accused guilty, the judge would surely have given him a prison sentence.

8 You must wash this sweater by hand.

9 We advise passengers travelling by air to wear comfortable clothing during long flights.

10 They are producing satellite dishes at the rate of 500 a week but they are selling slowly.

Verb Tenses (active and passive)

K *Put the verbs in brackets into the correct passive form.*

1 Foreign currency can (convert) into sterling at a number of points in the city, but the best rate and lowest commission charges (provide) at banks.

2 The impact of the postal strike began (feel) after only three days.

3 Visitors to the castle (show) around by an experienced guide. They not (allow) to wander around on their own.

4 The nuclear power station at Berkeley currently (decommission), but the process not (finish) for a hundred years.

5 Everyone (dress) up, as if they (invite) to a wedding.

6 Many medieval towns (damage) by fire because the houses (make) of wood.

7 By the end of next year, sixty houses (build) on that green field site.

8 Customers (ask) to ensure they (give) the correct change as mistakes cannot afterwards (rectify).

9 Trials now (conduct) to determine whether the aircraft is safe enough (use) by trainee pilots.

10 The identity of Jack the Ripper, a murderer responsible for a number of horrendous killings in the nineteenth century, never (establish).

Gerunds and Infinitives

A *Complete the sentences using either the infinitive or gerund as appropriate.*

1 In the canteen, you are only allowed .... food bought at the counter. (TO EAT/EATING)

2 .... is not allowed here. (TO SMOKE/SMOKING)

3 We don't allow .... in the private study area. (TO TALK/TALKING)

4 Mary needs .... more work if she is going to pass the test. (TO DO/DOING)

5 The carburettor needs .... before the car will run smoothly. (TO ADJUST/ADJUSTING)

6 Where can my pen be? I remember .... it when I made out that cheque in the bank. (TO HAVE/HAVING)

7 After having become World Junior Champion at the age of 13, Tom went on .... the Senior Championship. (TO WIN/WINNING)

8 What do you mean by not .... up? (TO TURN/TURNING)

9 If you go on .... so badly you will lose all your friends. (TO BEHAVE/BEHAVING)

10 John has always been extremely competitive. He means .... a millionaire by the time he is thirty. (TO BE/BEING)

B *(Follow the instructions in Exercise A)*

1 I love .... in my own country. I would hate .... abroad. (TO LIVE/LIVING)

2 Terry keeps on .... up Sandy, and she's just fed up with it. (TO RING/RINGING)

3 When you're older, you'll regret .... your time as a student. (TO WASTE/WASTING)

4 The Management regrets .... theatre-goers that tonight's performance has had to be cancelled. (TO INFORM/INFORMING)

5 .... payment of fares can lead to a penalty of £200. (TO AVOID/AVOIDING)

6 In order not to upset his colleagues, the accountant found it necessary .... about his salary. (TO LIE/LYING)

7 The shoplifter dreaded .... what would happen if he was found guilty of the offence. (TO THINK/THINKING)

8 Everyone was really looking forward to .... on holiday. (GO/GOING)

9 .... is a favourite hobby among retired people. (TO GARDEN/GARDENING)

10 Although put under great pressure during the police interrogation, the suspect refused .... that he had committed the robbery. (TO ADMIT/ADMITTING)

Gerunds and Infinitives

C *Put the verbs in brackets in the correct form, using either the gerund or infinitive.*

1 Unaccustomed as I am to public (speak).

2 If you speak aggressively about that politician he is bound to (retaliate).

3 The horse was close to (win) the race when it stumbled and fell.

4 After her husband's death at the hands of terrorists, May had to resign herself to (live) alone.

5 In this brief outline of the history of the town I shall confine myself to (talk) about major figures and events.

6 Caroline and Robert were supposed to (meet) us here half an hour ago. What can have happened to them?

7 Simon agreed to (help) with the preparations for the party.

8 The guest speaker failed to (turn) up at the conference.

9 The Prime Minister committed the Cabinet to (cut) the budget for health care.

10 Tonight I don't want to (go) out. I'd prefer to (stay) at home.

D *(Follow the instructions in Exercise C)*

1 After twelve hours of negotiation the two sides in the rail dispute are no nearer to (reach) agreement than they were at the start.

2 Who is likely to (succeed) the Prime Minister?

3 The duties of a nanny are limited to (look) after the children and do not extend to (help) with the housework.

4 I'm not used to (handle) this type of machinery, so could you possibly explain the instructions slowly?

5 The key to (create) a successful business is good management.

6 Alice was tempted to (apply) for the job when she heard about the salary package.

7 What led Robert to (tell) such lies?

8 People buying tickets before 30 April are entitled to (receive) a voucher for a discount in the restaurant.

9 The company has been commissioned to (undertake) a major research project.

10 I had to change the tyre myself. I couldn't get anyone to (help).

E *In the following exercise, rewrite the first sentence or sentences using a gerund construction after the words given. Make any other changes that are necessary, including inserting a preposition.*

EXAMPLE: It's Colin's job to hire and fire staff.
Colin's responsible ....
Colin's responsible for hiring and firing staff.

1 Harry and Sally have decided to share a flat in the centre of the city. I don't approve.
I don't approve ....

2 I don't like it when Peter comes home late.
I don't like ....

3 John has just been promoted. He's delighted.
John's delighted ....

4 The house is on the main road and that's what makes it difficult to sell.
It's the fact of ....

5 Employees are put out when they are paid late.
Employees are put out ....

6 I woke up when the baby started to cry.
I was woken up ....

7 Anna's mother was annoyed when Anna dropped the plate.
Anna's mother was annoyed ....

8 It's always expensive to buy a new house.
.... is always expensive.

9 We don't allow people to wear jeans in this disco.
.... is not allowed in this disco.

10 Andrew, I've just heard you've won the competition. Congratulations.
Andrew, congratulations ....

F *(Follow the instructions in Exercise E)*

1 In this company it's John who handles orders for new stock.
John is responsible ....

2 I don't believe my grandfather could commit a crime.
I don't believe my grandfather is capable ....

3 Amelia is proud that she passed her driving test first time.
Amelia is proud ....

4 'Sorry I'm late', said Jane.
Jane apologised ....

5 We think it was the girl's father who murdered her.
We suspect the girl's father ....

6 This area produces excellent beef.
This area is well-known ....

7 Charles collects first editions of twentieth-century authors.
Charles is interested ....

8 I wish Jake hadn't spent so much money on a new set of golf-clubs.
I'm annoyed ....

9 I don't mind living alone. I've done it for some years.
I'm used ....

10 Harriet would rather play tennis than go sailing.
Harriet is fonder ....

Gerunds and Infinitives

G *Put the verbs in the correct form, using either the gerund or infinitive (with or without* **to**).

I dread (think) what Mariana is going to do now that Tom has died. The house needs a lot (do) to it and she just can't afford (maintain) it. What she'd like (do) is (move) in with her son, but he lives fifty miles away. For Mariana that would mean (move) from familiar surroundings as well as (leave) the house. And I don't know that her son would really like (have) his mother with him. He's got three children of his own and they are allowed (do) what they want. They'd hate (be told) what to do by a granny who's just moved in. Remember what it was like when we were young – always hearing someone (say) 'Don't (do) this, stop (do) that.' Anyway Mariana will have (come) to a decision soon. She can't go on (live) in that house. Maybe she could sell it and buy something smaller. I hope she makes the right decision, and doesn't rush into something she will regret.

H *Complete these sentences with a passive infinitive or gerund, adding a preposition where necessary.*

EXAMPLES: These pills are (take) with a glass of water.
These pills are to be taken with a glass of water.

He lived in fear (arrest).
He lived in fear of being arrested.

1 Within twenty-four hours (release) prison, he had committed further offences.
2 After (examine) by a specialist, he agreed (operate on).
3 I am looking forward to going to the ball and (introduce) the prince.
4 The water-level is (check) every day as long as the drought continues.
5 These new regulations are (follow) all times.
6 The manager was in favour of new machinery (purchase).
7 These patrols are likely (ambush) before they get anywhere near their objective.
8 He was very anxious (interview).
9 The injured climbers had (lift) the mountain by helicopter.
10 The manuscript is believed (forge) the early nineteenth century.

Conditionals

A *Using the information given, make a sentence using **if**. Use one of the types of conditional sentences indicated in the examples.*

EXAMPLES: I may feel hungry later. In that case I'll eat the sandwiches in the fridge.
   If I feel hungry, I'll eat the sandwiches in the fridge.

   I don't feel tired so I'm not going to go to bed.
   If I felt tired, I would go to bed.

1 We plan to go abseiling on Sunday, but it all depends on the weather.

2 Tony doesn't show any interest in his schoolwork, but then his parents never encourage him.

3 I could enter the competition and I might possibly win.

4 The house is over there – only ten minutes' walk from here using the short cut across the park.

5 Sally keeps getting colds. She doesn't look after herself.

6 Robert works far too hard and is in danger of giving himself a heart attack.

7 The weather forecast says there will be a severe storm tonight. I'm worried about the hole in the roof.

8 It pays to keep the kitchen spotless, as it can be a major source of infection.

9 The train is already standing at the platform. You'd better run for it.

10 My advice to you is to make a clean breast of it.

B *Using the information given, make a sentence using **if**. Start with the words shown.*

EXAMPLE: It was raining so we stayed at home.
   If it hadn't been raining we wouldn't have stayed at home.

1 Martin didn't set his alarm. He woke up late.
   If Martin ....

2 Tom left the milk out of the fridge and it went off.
   The milk ....

3 Alison didn't get promoted so she resigned.
   If Alison ....

4 Chris had to walk home because he didn't have enough money for the bus fare.
   If Chris ....

5 The climbers were stranded when the weather deteriorated suddenly before they reached the summit.
   The climbers ....

6 The helicopter spotted the injured climber. As a result he was rescued.
   The injured climber ....

7 John invested all his savings in one company but then the company went into liquidation and he lost everything he had.
   John ....

8 Only by making a huge effort was the sales force able to achieve the target they had been set.
   The sales force ....

9 The crew acted swiftly in lowering the emergency chute and the passengers all escaped.
   If the crew ....

10 The teacher shortage was caused by a lack of planning on the part of the authorities.
   There ....

Conditionals

C *Using the information given, make a sentence using* **if**.

1 Thanks to the presence of a smoke detector the fire was discovered and dealt with in time.

2 There are no railings on that section of the river bank and that's why the child fell in.

3 The car ran out of petrol in the middle of the countryside. Not surprisingly, since Anthony didn't look at the fuel gauge once while he was driving.

4 There was a huge outcry mainly because the wood was destroyed in order to make way for the new motorway.

5 The disease spread rapidly because the health authorities failed to alert people to the danger.

6 The pipe cracked last winter because the water had not been disconnected.

7 The tomato plants were withering until Robert ensured they got a plentiful supply of fertiliser.

8 The earthquake caused a small amount of damage only because most of the houses had been specially constructed to withstand the shock.

9 Shirley phoned the service engineer to arrange a visit because the washing-machine was playing up.

10 Teresa got thin because she failed to eat what was necessary to maintain her body weight.

D *Using the information given, make a sentence using* **if**.

EXAMPLE: I've got toothache. I missed my last check-up at the dentist's.
I wouldn't have toothache now if I hadn't missed my last check-up at the dentist's.

1 Sam left the book on the grass and it rained. Now it's wet.

2 Billy can't understand what Madame Maurice is saying. He never made any effort to keep up his French after he left school.

3 Sarah spent the whole afternoon lying in the sun. Now she is complaining about being sunburnt.

4 Jane can't do her skirt up. She ate too much while on holiday.

5 The builder didn't do a good job when he put up the conservatory. It's letting in water now.

6 The family is heavily in debt. They have been living beyond their means since they bought their new house.

7 I can't offer you any biscuits. The children ate them all this morning.

8 We had the car serviced regularly. It's still running very smoothly.

9 The windows look spotlessly clean because the window-cleaner came yesterday.

10 I'm lost. I didn't bring a map.

Modals

A *Complete the following sentences, using* **shall**, **will** *or* **'ll** *as appropriate.*

1 .... that be all, madam?

2 Let's stay at home this evening, ... we?

3 'Who on earth is that ringing you at this time of night?' 'It .... be Tom.'

4 Robin is a very naughty child. He .... never do what he's told.

5 If you phone my secretary at 5, she .... be able to tell you the result.

6 I don't expect Claire .... be able to attend the meeting next week. We .... just have to forward the minutes to her afterwards.

7 'You .... never manage to get all that work done by tonight.' 'Oh yes I ....'

8 'The number you want is engaged,' said the operator. '............... I try it for you again later?'

9 I .... sign if you ....

10 It's best to have an early night as we .... be making an early start tomorrow.

B *Rewrite the following sentences using* **should**.

EXAMPLE: If you don't feel up to the job, you oughtn't to accept it.
   If you don't feel up to the job, you shouldn't accept it.

1 If you want to get a job in Sweden, don't you think it would be a good idea to start learning Swedish?

2 'Is the Prime Minister likely to resign during the present crisis?' 'In my opinion, it is most unlikely.'

3 If by any chance I were to die during the ascent of the mountain, this is what I would want as my epitaph: *Onwards and upwards.*

4 It isn't advisable to interrupt the boss at moments like this.

5 It was so kind of you to provide all this lovely food, but really it wasn't necessary.

6 I suggest we forget about our problems and go out and have a good time.

7 It wouldn't surprise me at all if Tim refused to contribute to Freda's leaving present, given all the backbiting that has gone on between them.

8 Rachel oughtn't to keep pestering her father while he's so busy.

9 It isn't very likely but it is possible I may be late. If I am, start the meeting without me.

10 It was wrong of Caroline to try to defraud the company she worked for.

Modals

C *Rewrite the following using* **may**.

EXAMPLE: Do you mind if I open the window?
May I open the window?

1 Could I possibly sit here?

2 In the mountains, you can never rule out the chance of an avalanche.

3 Although Sam is badly paid, he has never been tempted to resign because he finds the work so stimulating.

4 Perhaps Jim had to stay behind at work.

5 The view from the top was breathtaking, although getting to the top was really tough.

6 I'd like to speak to Mr Freeman, please.

7 Perhaps you don't remember me. I'm Frank Smith and we met on the training course in Exeter.

8 It's quite possible that no one will be at home.

9 If you carry an introduction from Professor Mulligan, the librarian could possibly be persuaded to let you in to see the manuscripts.

10 Of course, it is possible I am mistaken but aren't you the woman who was in the newspapers recently?

D *Sort the following sentences into three groups, according to the different ways in which* **might** *is used in each, and explain what each of these uses is.*

1 Perhaps next time you intend to advertise a post in my section, you might have the courtesy to let me know.

2 Ask Christine. She might know the answer.

3 Your job might be demanding, but at least it's interesting.

4 I'm not quite sure now, after all this time, but yes, Colin might have been present at the meeting.

5 Brian might get onto the short list, but I doubt if he will actually be offered the job.

6 'You might help', said Mary to Jack, who just sat there reading his newspaper.

7 Jason might have let me know he wasn't going to turn up before I went to the trouble of making a vegetarian meal for him.

8 Clive might have let you down, but you must realise that deep down, he really loves you.

9 I agree, it might not have been the singer's best performance. Nonetheless I enjoyed his singing immensely.

10 You never know who might turn up at a party like this.

E *Look at these sentences:*

We needn't have bought a Swedish phrase-book because we found when we arrived that everyone spoke English.
I didn't need to phone the railway station because there was a timetable with the letter confirming the date of the interview.

Now comment on the following sentences using **needn't have** *or* **didn't need to**.

1 I bought loads of suntan lotion but in fact it rained most of the time during our holiday.

2 Fortunately our holiday cottage had a welcome pack providing everything necessary for breakfast the following day.

3 I left the house an hour early because I expected the traffic to be bad, but there were no delays at all.

4 The hotel supplied towels for use at the swimming-pool.

5 I expected to spend Saturday cutting the grass, but the gardener had already done it.

6 The doctor is usually behind with appointments but this morning I was called straight in.

7 The candidate had prepared elaborate answers to a number of technical questions, but he was only asked for general information.

8 I was on the point of calling the stewardess when she arrived pushing the trolley of complimentary drinks.

9 John was really careful not to make any noise opening the door when he got home late, but his wife was waiting up for him.

10 Harriet went to great lengths to prepare a party for Louise's fifth birthday, but the poor child came down with measles the day before.

F *Classify the sentences according to the categories indicated by the six words below. Match the letters with the numbers.*

(a) opinion   (d) prohibition
(b) challenge   (e) fear
(c) annoyance   (f) courage

1 How dare you speak to me like that!

2 I dare say they'll get over their problems in time.

3 He was the first man to dare to climb Everest without oxygen.

4 I dare you to pick up that python.

5 Don't you dare come to this house again.

6 I just daren't mention it to him again. He gets so angry.

7 Dare you go on stage and help the magician?

8 You didn't dare say that to him, did you?

9 Dare to stand alone.

10 He was the only man who dared to stand up and protest.

11 I dare anyone to go three rounds with Bonecrusher Barnes.

12 He had obviously forgotten what had happened at their previous meeting and Fiona didn't dare remind him.

Modals

G *Make an appropriate comment in each of these situations, using* **dare**.

1 You see someone taking your bicycle without your permission.

2 You want to fight a duel.

3 You report to a friend that you wanted to ask your bank manager for more money, but didn't.

4 You tell someone that you think there will be a lot of snow this winter.

5 You describe what you have seen a lion tamer do.

6 You explain to a colleague why you didn't mention to your boss that it was very cold in the office.

7 You then challenge your colleague to complain to the boss about the heating.

8 You are furious when a shop assistant refuses to accept responsibility for selling damaged goods.

9 You express admiration to a student who approached a celebrated pianist to ask her about a particular interpretation of a piece of music.

10 You agree with a colleague that John is a good worker but do not believe he is up to promotion.

Reported Speech

A *Change the following statements into reported speech.*

1 'The guests will be leaving at twelve o'clock,' said Michael.

2 'The special offer ends on Saturday,' said the man on TV.

3 'Mary is feeling a bit depressed,' said Gladys.

4 'The Fraud Investigation Team has discovered some disturbing information about Mr Fletcher's business activities,' said the detective.

5 'The committee will be discussing the plans for the new building,' said the Chairman.

6 'The patrol rescued three men from the crashed helicopter,' said the sergeant.

7 'The survey team has been exploring the Mato Grosso for several weeks,' said Professor Challenger.

8 'All the instruments must be re-tested,' said the production manager.

9 'The information Mr Moriarty asked for cannot be provided,' said the registrar.

10 'All the furniture is going to be replaced,' said the office manager.

B *Report these sentences. Assume that the time and place are quite different from those of the original statements.*

1 'I want to finish this job today,' said the painter.

2 'We will be able to start work at the beginning of next week,' said the foreman.

3 'I haven't eaten since yesterday,' said Janet.

4 'Everything was arranged yesterday morning,' said Michael.

5 'Everything will have been planted by the end of this year,' said the gardener.

6 'Steven is going to meet me here tomorrow,' said Jessica.

7 'The interview took place this morning,' said the principal.

8 'Both my daughters are going to get married early next year,' said Mr Parkinson.

9 'The last total eclipse of the sun was five years ago,' said Mr Moore.

10 'It is essential that you pay the extra duty now,' said the customs officer.

Reported Speech

C *Report these questions.*

1 'When did you start getting severe headaches, Mrs Bell?' asked Dr Fox.

2 'How did the animals escape from the cage?' asked the zoo-keeper.

3 'Why were no safety checks carried out before take-off?' asked the barrister.

4 'What has been done to help the homeless?' asked the Prince.

5 'Which machine did best in the tests?' the journalists wanted to know.

6 'Who will be the first to reach the summit?' wondered Edmund.

7 'Do I need to be a member to use the gym?' asked Arnold.

8 'Who won?' asked Harry.

9 'How is your head, Jack?' asked Jill.

10 'Must duty be paid on the goods?' enquired Mr Smart.

D *Report the following statements, using the words in capitals.*

EXAMPLE: 'The ice is not safe to skate on,' said Uncle George.   (WARN/CHILDREN)
Uncle George warned the children that the ice was not safe to skate on.

1 'Those mountains are full of bandits,' said Robin.   (WARN/ME)

2 'Don't forget your compass,' said Rebecca.   (REMIND/HIM)

3 'You will leave the hotel at seven a.m.,' said the courier.   (INFORM/GROUP)

4 'Congratulations on winning first prize,' said Frank.   (CONGRATULATE/ME)

5 'It's your fault we are late,' said Elizabeth.   (BLAME/ME)

6 'There is a fax for you,' said Bill.   (TELL/ME)

7 'Carry these ammunition boxes to the forward positions,' said the captain.   (ORDER/SOLDIERS)

8 'Thank you for looking after the children,' said Miranda.   (THANK/ALICE)

9 'I really will be at the airport to meet you,' said Timothy.   (PROMISE/HIS SISTER)

10 'Three of the interviewees have cancelled their appointments,' said my secretary. (INFORM/ME)

E *(Follow the instructions in Exercise **D**)*

1 'I will not accept this contract,' said Sheila.   (REFUSE)

2 'I'm sorry I didn't finish the report on time,' said Nigel.   (APOLOGISE)

3 'I disposed of the bodies,' said Nick.   (ADMIT)

4 'Profits have risen by twenty per cent this year,' said the chairman.   (STATE)

5 'The delay occurred because of a mechanical problem,' said the information officer.
  (EXPLAIN)

6 'The new camera will be the best on the market,' said the salesman.   (CLAIM)

7 'I did not take part in the robbery,' said Jeff.   (DENY)

8 'What about driving up to the Lakes?' said Fiona.   (SUGGEST)

9 '.............. and turnover has increased by fifteen per cent,' said the chairman.   (ADDED)

10 'All the vehicles are in a satisfactory condition,' said the inspector.   (REPORT)

Sentence Synthesis

A *Choose the correct ending (A, B or C) for each sentence.*

1 He rode to Ghent as fast as he could because
  A his horse was exhausted.
  B the message was extremely urgent.
  C he arrived in the nick of time.

2 He packed his suitcase the night before so that
  A he didn't have to hurry in the morning.
  B it always took him a long time to do.
  C there was only just enough room for everything.

3 James entered the competition but
  A he knew he would win.
  B he had recently been injured.
  C he wasn't very confident of success.

4 By Sunday evening, Roger had no money left although
  A he had spent it all.
  B he had withdrawn £300 from the bank on Friday afternoon.
  C he was very upset about it.

5 John had so much work to do that
  A he was already very busy.
  B he didn't know where to start.
  C he was able to complete it.

B *Rewrite these sentences using one or two present participles.*

EXAMPLES: I picked up the book. I found my place. I began to read.
  Picking up the book and finding my place, I began to read.

  When he reached the docks, he saw the ship sailing into the distance.
  Reaching the docks, he saw the ship sailing into the distance.

1 I held the rifle firmly. I took aim. I pulled the trigger.

2 Roland trembled with fear. He shivered with cold. He entered the tower.

3 I didn't have my keys. I couldn't start the car.

4 He didn't look at me. He took the money. (Without ....)

5 He saw the Pacific for the first time. He stood silent and amazed. (On ....)

6 He felt incredibly exhilarated. He pushed aside the stone that blocked the way to the Pharaoh's tomb.

7 When I found no one at home, I immediately telephoned the police.

8 I tore the secret letter into pieces, put it in my mouth and forced myself to swallow it.

9 Michael stretched out his arm and wrenched the statue from its niche.

10 Since I didn't want to seem stupid, I said nothing at all.

C *Rewrite the following sentences using either a present or past participle in the first part of the sentence.*

EXAMPLES: He lives in the country and is accustomed to the sight and smell of farm animals.
Living in the country, he is accustomed to the sight and smell of farm animals.

He was born in Bradford and emigrated to Australia in his early twenties.
Born in Bradford, he emigrated to Australia in his early twenties.

---

1 You will be aged 30–40 and have already carved out an ambitious career path.

2 You should be educated to degree standard and you should be able to analyse complex problems and explain them in language suitable for the layman.

3 You will hold a recognised qualification in this field and will have at least five years' experience in a managerial role.

4 If you join our company you will have the chance to develop new skills.

5 You will report to the Financial Director and you will be responsible for the production and presentation of all financial information.

6 You will be based at our Basingstoke headquarters where you will enjoy all the facilities of a modern office.

7 You will work in a busy environment and you need to be capable of meeting deadlines.

8 We employ over 2,000 staff and we can offer the full range of company benefits.

9 Salaries which range from £30–45,000 are enhanced by a bonus scheme and company car.

10 Our company will give you every opportunity for personal and professional development and your career will blossom.

D *Add commas where it is appropriate to do so in these sentences.*

1 Samuel Browne whom you met last week will be visiting the office on Tuesday.

2 John Speke who discovered the source of the Nile was killed in a hunting accident.

3 I was delighted when he gave me a copy of 'The Woodlanders' which had been signed by the author.

4 The lady whose dog you kicked has complained to the police.

5 I spoke to Her Royal Highness for two minutes which was incredibly exciting.

6 It happened in a town whose name I can't recall.

7 The regulation that you are in breach of is Number 2/4677(b).

8 This is my cousin who will explain the system to you.

9 Martin had to visit the dentist again which he hated.

10 The Duke of Wellington whose socks he bid for at an auction is one of David's heroes.

Sentence Synthesis

E *Join the sentences together using* **none, neither, all, some, both, a few,** *or* **a little,** *and a relative pronoun.*

EXAMPLES: They offered me some cake. I ate a little of it.
They offered me some cake, a little of which I ate.

There were seven people at the meeting. I knew all of them.
There were seven people at the meeting, all of whom I knew.

1 He showed me two jackets. I didn't like either of them.

2 He introduced me to three people. I hadn't met any of them before.

3 We saw three films. I had seen them all before.

4 There were at least twenty people there. I didn't know any of them.

5 Seven people applied for the job. Some of them were very well-qualified.

6 She offered me some orange-juice. I drank a little of it.

7 On the table were several oatcakes. I ate a few of them.

8 He gave me two books. I had read both before.

9 They delivered one hundred machines. None of them worked properly.

10 He has two sisters. They are both doctors.

F *Complete the gaps with one of these words or phrases:*

since	*much as*	*as soon as*	*as though*	*to some extent*
in case	*however*	*in order to*	*considering*	*as long as*

1 .... I like John, I can't support him on this issue.

2 .... hard he tried, he still couldn't understand the computer manual.

3 They took ice-axes with them .... they needed to cut steps in the ice.

4 We have nothing to fear from our enemies .... we keep our nerve.

5 .... that this is John's first competition, he has achieved a very respectable score.

6 He became an American citizen .... promote his business interests.

7 'It looks .... the same man committed both crimes,' said Inspector Morse.

8 While I accept your arguments ...., I cannot support the action you are taking.

9 '............................ the enemy crosses the stream, open fire!' said the captain.

10 .... I knew the mountain path like the back of my hand, I was able to travel at a fast pace.

G *Complete the gaps with one of these words and phrases:*

> *as if*   *whenever*   *anywhere*   *everywhere*   *for fear that*
> *the same way* *seeing that* *directly*   *no matter*   *by the time*

1 .... they heard the bell, the penguins rushed to the edge of the pool.

2 You have to dismantle the radio .... as the instructor did.

3 .... he looked, the Health Inspector found grease and grime.

4 He hung his food high up in the trees .... the bears would steal it during the night.

5 .... you've already done an initial training course, you needn't come to the pre-course induction.

6 You can pitch your tents .... you like.

7 .... how much money the gangsters offered him, the judge refused to take a bribe.

8 He behaved .... he thought he was being followed.

9 .... he came to, night had fallen and he found himself alone in the desert.

10 .... he heard the good news, he phoned his parents.

H *Can you say what is wrong with these sentences found in signs, advertisements and newspapers, and rewrite them so that the meaning is clearer?*

1 Old English Sheepdog for sale. Will eat anything. Especially fond of children.

2 There was a skeleton staff at the hospital.

3 Will ladies responsible for making the tea kindly empty the teapots and kettles, then stand upside down in the sink.

4 FOUR MINUTE RAIDERS GRAB £2 MILLION.

5 The exhibition is well worth viewing. It features the work of three British craftsmen's woven rugs.

6 Being a small college, everyone can get to know everyone else.

7 As a boy, his mother had neglected him.

8 The explosives were found by a security man in a plastic bag.

9 Eating grass, he saw a cow.

10 CHAMPION WEIGHTLIFTER FINED FOR SHOPLIFTING.

Sentence Synthesis

I *Using the first sentence as the main clause, combine the sentences in each of the following examples to make one new sentence. In each sentence you will need to use at least one item from List A and one from List B.*

EXAMPLES: He sold the farm.
His family had owned it for centuries.
He was desperately short of cash.
Although his family had owned the farm for centuries, he sold it because he was desperately short of cash.

A	B
although	because
as	but
even if	in case
whenever	in order to
where	so .... that
which	unless
while	whereas
whose	who

1 They cut down the trees.
The trees had been there for sixty years.
Their purpose was to sell the timber.

2 He returned to the village.
He had been born and brought up there.
It had changed beyond recognition.

3 He walked across the common.
It was wet and muddy.
This would save him at least ten minutes.

4 Hans took a rope-ladder with him.
He stayed in hotels.
They might catch fire.

5 It was cold.
He suffered frostbite in several toes.
He wore several pairs of socks.

6 The price of cabbages has doubled.
The weather has been extremely poor.
The price of potatoes has remained steady.
Supplies have been imported from Egypt.

7 He swallowed the fish's eye.
It made him feel sick.
He wanted to impress his friends.

8 He wrote a letter to Mr and Mrs Edwards.
He had stayed in their house for eight weeks.
He gave a series of lectures at the university.
He thanked them for their hospitality.

9 Candidates will not be interviewed for this post.
They have extremely good qualifications.
They have at least five years' experience.

10 He sold the painting.
He was short of money.
His grandfather had given it to him.
His grandfather had known the artist well.

J *Join the following sentences together to make one sentence.*

1 Eyestrain may occur.
It will lead to headaches.
It will lead to lack of concentration.
These may occur when the machine is used for long periods.
There are some precautions that will reduce the problem.
You can take these precautions.

2 It is important to avoid glare.
You can do this by making sure that the brightness control is correctly adjusted.
You can also position the screen so that there is no external reflection.

3 You may take these precautions.
You may continue to feel uncomfortable.
If this happens you should fit special filters.
These are fitted over the screen.
They eliminate glare completely.

4 Accidental loss of material could be catastrophic.
This information is stored on disk.
This is why you should make copies of all disks.
You will need the copies for everyday use.

5 Make sure the disk drive is empty.
Do this before you switch on or off.
The reason for this is that disks will be damaged.
Sudden surges of power cause this damage.

6 Disks should be carefully labelled.
Do this as soon as you have saved anything on them.
You may assume an unlabelled disk is blank.
You may be careless.
You may wipe out an unlabelled disk.
This disk may contain valuable information.

7 The Pantheon is one of the finest Roman buildings.
It is in Rome itself.
It was built on the orders of the Emperor Hadrian.
It has inspired many later buildings.

8 In the fifth century the Goths entered the Pantheon.
They did this after they had attacked and captured Rome.
They intended to destroy the Pantheon.
The beauty of its interior stopped them in their tracks.
The Pantheon has survived to this day.
Its beauty is relatively intact.

9 There is tremendous public demand for our products.
This demand has been aided by extensive television coverage.
It has ensured that production is at an all-time high.
The enthusiasm and dedication of staff is also at an all-time high.

10 It is only three years since we moved to our present site.
This is hard to believe.
It is now one of the most advanced and productive factories in the U.K.

Adjectives, Adverbs and Inversion

A *Put the adjectives in front of the noun in the correct order. Include **a** or **an** where appropriate.*

1	girl	French, clever
2	church	beautiful, medieval
3	skirt	long, cotton, blue
4	car	new, expensive
5	farmhouse	large, medieval, well-preserved
6	figure	small, white, porcelain
7	chair	very fine, oak, carved, Elizabethan
8	news	alarming, recent
9	carpet	red, Persian, silk, expensive
10	politician	young, ambitious
11	umbrella	old, rather battered
12	wine	delightful, French, country
13	house	four-bedroomed, detached, well-maintained
14	pie	apple, delicious, hot
15	telephone	modern, wall-mounted, easy-to-dial
16	flask	stainless steel, large, unbreakable
17	man	well-built, bearded, tall
18	novel	first, promising
19	thesis	thoroughly researched, well-written
20	beach	long, completely deserted, clean

B *Complete the sentences with one of the following:*

ablaze	*afloat*	*alive*	*alone*	*asleep*
blazing	*floating*	*live*	*lone*	*sleeping*

1 When they noticed that the ship they had abandoned was still .... the sailors got back on board.

2 Rescue ships collected the .... debris in case it revealed clues as to why the aircraft had crashed into the sea.

3 Frank Winchester, the famous .... yachtsman, is nearing the end of his round-the-world voyage.

4 The oil refinery was completely .... within seconds of the bombs being dropped.

5 The three climbers were found .... after being trapped on the glacier for seven days.

6 The firemen entered the .... building to find out if people were trapped.

7 Mrs Green lived .... for the last years of her life.

8 'Let .... dogs lie,' as the proverb says.

9 'Don't touch those wires! They are ....!' said the electrician.

10 The children are fast ....

Adjectives, Adverbs and Inversion

C *Complete the sentences with **still** or **yet**.*

1 His latest novel is his best ....

2 As .... we have received no answer to our letter.

3 Telephone Martin about it, or, better ...., go round and see him.

4 He worked very hard, ... he failed to achieve his ambitions.

5 It takes a long time by bus. ...., it's cheap and reliable.

6 I have warned him countless times but he .... arrives late.

7 The doctor is .... examining his last patient.

8 Despite the fire damage to our store, we are .... in business.

9 Our company has, over the years, become strong and mighty, and if we all work together it can become mightier ....

10 I've tried phoning him many times but I .... can't get through.

D *Complete the sentences with **fairly, quite** or **rather**.*

1 This composition is .... good but you could do better.

2 He looks .... pale, doesn't he?

3 Those apples aren't very good but I think you'll find these red ones are .... sweet.

4 I thought the hotel was .... expensive considering how far it was from the centre.

5 In my opinion, she telephones you .... too often.

6 Are you sure the snake is .... dead?

7 .... honestly, I think he is .... inefficient.

8 I've got a .... good memory for names, but I'm .... bad on dates.

9 Have another cup of tea – it's still .... hot.

10 I thought this exercise was going to be .... easy but in fact it was .... difficult.

E *Complete the sentences with* **so** *or* **such**.

1 It was .... a serious illness that he was off work for seven months.

2 .... few people turned up for the fete, that the committee decided not to hold any more.

3 .... was his temper that on this occasion no one dared to approach him.

4 The children behaved .... badly that their mother felt quite embarrassed.

5 '............... dedication to art is rarely seen in one .... young,' said the judge.

6 'This is .... serious a matter that I have no choice but to call in the police,' said the headmaster.

7 .... confused was he that he forgot to sign the cheque.

8 You can return the books late but if you do .... you have to pay a fine.

9 He had never been .... happy before in his entire life.

10 You can pay in full now if you .... wish.

F *Complete the second sentence so that it means the same as the first. Make any grammatical changes that may be necessary.*

EXAMPLE:　It isn't as hot today as it was yesterday.
Yesterday it was ....
Yesterday it was hotter than it is today.

1 Fewer people attended the committee meeting than the Chairman had expected.
There weren't ....

2 Robert and Jilly see less of their daughter than they would like to.
Robert and Jilly don't see ....

3 Joan is better qualified than the other members of the department.
The other members of the department ....

4 Frank's car goes much faster than Dan's.
Dan's car doesn't go ....

5 Jim usually drinks a lot of beer but he didn't on Saturday night.
Jim didn't ....

6 This is the nicest place I've ever been.
Nowhere ....

7 This is the worst thing I've heard.
Nothing ....

8 Canada is a much less densely populated country than Britain.
Britain ....

9 Tom's behaviour was far worse than anyone else's.
No one else ....

10 I don't care how much fuss you make, you're not making me change my mind.
You can make ....

Adjectives, Adverbs and Inversion

G *The following sentences show inversion of subject and verb. Rewrite them without inversion.*

EXAMPLE: Rarely has the team received such an ovation as when they won the World Cup.
The team has rarely received such an ovation as when they won the World Cup.

1 Not only did I wish to register my disapproval but also to bring about a change in policy.

2 Not until the end of the match did our team manage to assert its superiority.

3 Only when the last competitors had completed the course did the captain allow himself to celebrate his team's victory.

4 Not since his earliest years had Thomas felt so carefree.

5 Only once has this runner's performance been bettered.

6 Such was the King's displeasure that he determined to rid himself of his advisors.

7 So enchanted was the composer with the beauty of the actress that he determined there and then that she was to be his wife.

8 Seldom are swans seen on this stretch of the river.

9 Only if you practise every day will you become a proficient pianist.

10 Hardly had Simon completed a three-month overseas assignment before he was being pressed to take another.

H *Rewrite the sentences using the introductory words given.*

1 You won't find fossils like this anywhere else.
Nowhere else ....

2 He tried to revive his comrade, but in vain.
In vain ....

3 The hurricane winds were so strong that no building in the town escaped damage.
So strong ....

4 It was only recently that the cause of cystic fibrosis was discovered.
Only recently ....

5 Harry was sent to prison once and is determined never to be sent there again.
Harry is determined that never again ....

6 Friends and relatives seeing passengers off are not allowed into the departure lounge under any circumstances.
Under no circumstances ....

7 I didn't believe Jane's explanation for one moment.
Not for one moment ....

8 It was only when I heard the full story that I realised I had been taken in.
Only when ....

9 Their fear of the occupying army was so great that few of the inhabitants were prepared to resist.
So great ....

10 You will be entitled to a reduction in the membership fee only if you fall into one of the following categories.
Only if ....

I *Rewrite the sentences using the introductory words given, and invert where necessary.*

1 John broke the rules just once, but he suffered the consequences for the rest of his life.
Only once ....

2 The demonstrator explained the procedure twice but the trainees still failed to understand.
Even after a second explanation ....

3 The authorities are prepared to allow exceptions to the rule in very few cases.
In very few cases ....

4 Surely Tim would have accepted the job if the salary package had been more attractive.
No doubt ....

5 There was concern about potential damage to the environment even in the 1950's.
Even in the 1950's ....

6 Sheila hardly ever opens her mouth at staff meetings.
Hardly ever ....

7 The candidate's mind went blank every time he was asked a question.
On every occasion ....

8 It was good to see that in a few cases there was an astonishing response.
In a few cases ....

9 The office manager was unwilling to tolerate the level of absenteeism any longer.
No longer ....

10 I will repeat the information once only.
Only once ....

Prepositions

A *Complete the sentences with:* **above, over.**

1 'Nobody on the staff is .... suspicion,' said Detective Inspector Dixon.

2 Your marks have been .... average all year.

3 When you have read this document, please distribute it to the people named ....

4 He held a handkerchief .... his face as he escaped from the blazing building.

5 They discussed the matter .... a cup of tea.

6 The waiters received tips .... and .... their wages.

7 This product is used all .... the world.

8 .... all, remember to lock the money in the safe at the end of the day.

9 The policeman placed a sheet .... the bodies.

10 Seen from ...., the marks on the Martian surface look remarkably like canals.

B *Complete the sentences with:* **below, beneath, under.**

1 Boxers are forbidden to punch .... the belt.

2 The temperature dropped .... freezing-point.

3 Jack cannot drink in a pub because he is .... age.

4 With regard to the thefts, several members of staff are .... suspicion.

5 The trade union leader said that the workers who had not supported the strike were .... contempt.

6 Because the village is several metres .... sea-level, it is frequently flooded.

7 When Lady Anthea de Montmorency married Fred Glubb, a lorry driver from Peckham, her family thought she had married .... her.

8 .... Queen Victoria, Britain's economy expanded at a rapid pace.

9 He spoke to us .... his breath.

10 We saw the film entitled '.............. the Planet of the Apes'.

C *Complete the sentences using* **as** *or* **like** *as appropriate.*

1 After graduating with a degree in chemistry Jane landed a job .... a trainee stockbroker.

2 When Charles went to Malaga he stayed in the same hotel .... I did.

3 Just .... me, Michael would rather spend a free afternoon with his feet up reading a book than going for a five-mile walk.

4 .... her mother Elizabeth is .... stubborn .... a mule.

5 Tom's just .... a child when it comes to eating sweets.

6 She works for the local council .... an accountant.

7 Dressed up in those furs you look .... a Russian princess.

8 .... far .... I am concerned, that is the end of the affair.

9 Many people regard Emily Bronte .... one of the greatest poets of the nineteenth century.

10 You should be more friendly towards people, ... Neil.

D *Complete the sentences with the correct preposition.*

1 The lorry collided .... a fork-lift truck.

2 Janet and John share an interest .... ornithology.

3 Albert has suffered .... asthma for a number of years.

4 Compared .... his previous work, this latest novel is disappointing.

5 The forward positions have been .... attack for the last nine hours.

6 The patient would not consent .... the operation.

7 .... most cases, there will be no additional fee to pay.

8 All the conspirators were condemned .... death.

9 The party leader distanced himself .... his more extreme supporters.

10 The soldiers had little respect .... their officers.

Prepositions

E *Complete the sentences with the correct preposition.*

1 He is talking to the man .... a beard who is standing next to the woman .... the red dress.

2 All the children were dressed .... blue.

3 When he was fifteen he ran away .... sea.

4 They are both .... their fifties.

5 Captain Baxter was a man .... great courage.

6 'I am .... my prime,' said Miss Brodie.

7 Simon helped the man .... crutches to cross the road.

8 Here is the patient .... malaria, doctor.

9 Professor Urquell has an I.Q. .... 160.

10 The two children, a boy .... six and a girl .... ten, were not injured in the accident.

F *Complete the sentences with the correct preposition.*

1 I don't know his name but I know him .... sight.

2 You have been arrested .... conspiring .... others to commit a breach .... the peace.

3 Your lives will be .... risk if you continue the journey.

4 We can offer you £500 .... advance and the rest when the job is finished.

5 Please answer this letter .... return.

6 I am afraid I don't have the figures .... hand but I can obtain them by tomorrow.

7 As a junior doctor, you must be .... call twenty-four hours a day.

8 Mr Jenkins cannot work for any other company because he is .... contract to us.

9 I hope that you will bear these factors .... mind when making your report.

10 You can have a suit made .... measure .... a very reasonable price.

Vocabulary

A *Complete the sentences with one of the following:*

all together	alternate	alternative	altogether	coast
disinterested	economic	economical	shore	uninterested

1 The doctor comes on .... Tuesdays.

2 Have you any .... proposals?

3 I want you to sing ....

4 That's £11.25 ....

5 The ship was ten miles off the French ....

6 I picked up these pebbles on the .... of Lake Titicaca.

7 It is more .... to buy in bulk.

8 He wrote 'The .... History of Britain 1750–1914'.

9 Only a person with a .... approach will be acceptable as mediator to both management and trade unions.

10 He was .... in the job he was doing so he decided to leave.

B *Choose one word from each of the ten pairs of words to fit the appropriate sentence.*

efficient/effective	**migrate/emigrate**
injure/damage	**industrial/industrious**
household/householder	**accept/agree**
manifestation/demonstration	**conscious/conscientious**
memories/memoirs	**intolerable/intolerant**

1 At the end of the summer you can see the swallows gathering to
.... south.

2 After his defeat in the general election, the Prime Minister retired to write his
....

3 If John keeps on working so hard he will .... his health.

4 We moved from Birmingham to an area that was less ....

5 All right, I .... to do just as you wish.

6 Thirty-five people were arrested following the .... against the government's policies.

7 'I give £50 a week to my mother to help with .... expenses,' Julie told her friends.

8 'I find the pupils' behaviour ....' said the new teacher.

Vocabulary

9 This cream is very .... against most types of skin rash.

10 Helen was a marvellous pupil, always .... of those areas where she needed to improve.

C *Choose one word from each of the ten pairs of words to fit the appropriate sentence.*

actually/presently	economy/saving
bank/bench	embark/board
clothes/cloths	fantasy/imagination
delighted/delightful	female/feminine
refuse/deny	homework/housework

1 This is .... news. So, when's the wedding day?

2 Sam sat down on the .... in the park and watched the people walking by.

3 What kind of .... do you make by buying in bulk?

4 Passengers may .... up to three hours before the sailing time.

5 Joan has a terrific .... I just don't know where she gets her ideas from.

6 Mary was so hard up she decided she could no longer afford to pay someone else to help her with her ....

7 The .... of the species is the deadlier of the two.

8 I can't .... that the singer has charm, but his voice is not to my taste.

9 Have you got any old .... I can use when I clean the engine?

10 'Is she a new secretary?' '..., she's the accountant.'

D *Choose one word from each of the ten pairs of words to fit the appropriate sentence.*

suit/suite	convinced/persuaded
discover/invent	credible/creditable
treat/cure	custom/habit
definite/definitive	classic/classical
historic/historical	prevent/avoid

1 Jenny likes nothing better than to curl up on the sofa with a thick .... novel.

2 One way to .... tooth decay is to put fluoride in the drinking water.

3 So finally a bronze medal for Jane Smith. All in all, a very .... performance from a girl who's only seventeen.

4 John always says how lovely it would be to spend more time together, but it's never possible to pin him down to a .... arrangement.

5 We decided that the bathroom .... just had to be sage green.

6 It's always difficult to change your lifestyle, but one .... that I decided I just had to break was eating chocolate in the middle of the afternoon.

7 Jon and Tara both love .... music.

8 All these arguments about how horoscopes really reflect day-to-day events are all very well, but I'm not ....

9 The doctors decided to .... Mary's cancer with chemotherapy.

10 How long will it be before they .... a solution to world poverty?

E *Choose one word from each of the ten pairs of words to fit the appropriate sentence.*

notorious/famous	**imply/infer**
sensible/sensitive	**stationery/stationary**
beside/besides	**human/humane**
affect/effect	**exhausting/exhaustive**
aloud/loudly	**comprehensive/understandable**

1 Harry's not a careful driver. Only last week he pulled out from behind a .... vehicle straight into the path of an oncoming lorry.

2 What are you trying to ....? That I'm not telling the truth?

3 The kennels was closed down after the local council investigated and found no evidence of the .... treatment advertised by the owners.

4 Every drug that is put on the market has undergone .... tests.

5 Don't pay too much attention to what I said just now. I was really only thinking

....

6 Everyone is worried about just what impact the greenhouse .... will have.

7 People with .... skin should always wear rubber gloves when doing the washing-up.

8 The Marsh Murderers are .... for the torture and brutal killing of their child victims.

9 So, Mandy, ... decorating your house, what else do you enjoy doing in your spare time?

10 It's quite .... why Jackie doesn't get on with her parents. They continue to treat her like a small child.

Vocabulary

F *Complete the sentences with the correct form of one of the following:* **hope, expect, wait (for).**

1 John .... to go to university, but it all depends on his exam results.

2 There is no point in hurrying to get to the bus stop. I .... the bus will be late as usual.

3 Mrs Brown is .... her second baby at the end of June.

4 The Prime Minister said that he .... to win the election easily since his party had a strong lead in the opinion polls.

5 The aeroplane is on the runway .... permission to take off.

6 The engineers .... to finish the bridge by June but bad weather may delay them.

7 We .... them at 7 p.m. It's now 9 p.m. I do .... they haven't had an accident. We'll .... another half-hour before calling the police.

8 The manager cannot see you until 11 a.m. Would you like to .... or make an appointment for tomorrow?

9 'England .... that every man will do his duty,' said Admiral Nelson on the eve of battle.

10 This accommodation is not up to the standard I ....

G *Complete the sentences with one of the following:*

last	**at last**	**at least**	**late**	**latest**
least	**last but not least**	**eventually**	**in the end**	**at the end**

1 He tried, without success to trace his long-lost brother but, ..., after several years he gave up.

2 I must add that we are also grateful to Mrs Hibberd for allowing us to use the school, and, ..., I'd like to thank Mrs Roberts for providing us with such delicious food.

3 This is the .... version of this highly successful model.

4 You can tell by the engine number that this was the .... Ford Capri to roll off the production line.

5 .... of the interview he was asked to wait outside the room.

6 ...., he persuaded the squirrel to sit on his hand and eat nuts.

7 In the circumstances, the .... he can do is apologise.

8 'You are not just ....,' said the headmaster. 'You are the .... boy to arrive!'

9 'Home ....!' said Elizabeth as she stepped over the threshold.

10 A house in this area will cost .... £100,000.

H *Complete the sentences with one of the following:* **life, living, live, alive, lives**.

1 WANTED: OUTLAW JESSE JAMES – DEAD OR ....

2 Don't touch that electrical wire – it's ....

3 The cost of .... has risen by 20% this year.

4 Harriet found it difficult to adjust to the way of .... on the island.

5 She has written a book called 'The .... of Famous Women'.

6 Bernard is always the .... and soul of the party.

7 He found it difficult to make a .... as a musician and decided to gain further skills.

8 The football match will be broadcast ....

9 The painting of a vase of flowers was entitled 'Still ....'.

10 In his report, Frederick described the appalling .... conditions of the workers.

I *Complete the sentences with the correct form of one of the following:*

| break up | crumble | decay | decline | decompose |
| disperse | dissolve | go off | peter out | shatter |

1 Edward Gibbon wrote 'The .... and Fall of the Roman Empire'.

2 The windscreen .... when a stone flew up from the road.

3 The seam of coal was quite wide near the entrance to the mine but it soon ....

4 He .... the biscuits in order to make the base for a cheesecake.

5 By the time the police found the body, it was badly ....

6 'I'm afraid some of your teeth have .... quite badly,' said the dentist.

7 We can't eat this meat. It has definitely ....

8 The police .... the crowd with water-hoses.

9 If you prefer, you can .... the tablets in water before taking them.

10 The ship was stuck on the rocks and .... over the next few days.

Vocabulary

J *Complete these sentences with a word for a part of the body.*

EXAMPLE: They clapped their *hands*.

1 He nodded his ....

2 He clenched his ....

3 He flexed his ....

4 She folded her ....

5 He cracked his ....

6 She snapped her ....

7 The fortune-teller read my ....

8 She filed her ....

9 He shrugged his ....

10 She stamped her ....

11 He craned his ....

12 She pursed her ....

13 She plucked her ....

14 The soldiers swung their ....

15 Her dancing partner trod on her ....

16 His .... chattered with cold.

17 There were goose-pimples all over his ....

18 He rubbed his .... together to keep warm.

19 He felt butterflies in his ....

20 It is a ....-chilling story of demonic revenge.

K *Use these words in the sentences that follow. You will sometimes have to change the form of the word to fit the grammar of the sentence, especially if it is used as a verb.*

beaver	duck	hound	rat	wasp
cat	elephant	mammoth	sardine	whale
crow	fish	pig	sheep	wolf
dog	guinea-pig	rabbit	stag	worm

1 Nobody ever questions her leadership. They just follow like ....

2 We need fifteen students to act as .... in an educational experiment.

3 Everybody had a .... of a time at summer camp.

4 This really is a .... task. We can't finish it by the end of the month.

5 I try and avoid talking to Antonia because she's always .... on about something silly.

6 All his life, Schubert was .... by bad luck.

7 His creditors .... him for the money he owed them.

8 She is always making .... remarks about other women.

9 'There is something very .... about this case,' said Detective Inspector Mills.

10 After twenty years in advertising, Jonathan decided to leave the .... race and buy a farm in Wales.

11 Don't make a .... of yourself. Eat more carefully.

12 He was so hungry he .... his food down.

13 Edward never forgets the smallest detail. He has a memory like an
....

14 '............................!' shouted our sergeant as the bullets whizzed over our heads.

15 In order to carry out industrial espionage, he .... his way into the chairman's confidence.

16 We were packed in the train like ....

17 Don't get upset by what Norman says. He is inclined to make .... remarks.

18 He is still .... away at his analysis of Shakespeare's grammar.

19 The night before his wedding Ian held a .... party.

20 She's not a very good sport. She gets depressed when she loses and .... with delight when she wins.

L *Complete these sentences with one of the following:*

commentary	**debate**	**dialect**	**jargon**	**inaugural address**
patter	**soliloquy**	**sermon**	**maiden speech**	**speech impediment**

1 The bishop's .... went on for two hours and most of the congregation fell asleep.

2 Mr MacGregor will make his .... in the House of Commons on Tuesday.

3 The actor moved to the front of the stage and gave Hamlet's famous 'To be or not to be'
....

4 Their conversation was peppered with the .... of the advertising profession, so it was not always easy to follow.

5 The second person to speak in the ...., against the motion, was the president of the society.

6 All the salesmen were trained to learn their sales .... by heart.

7 The farmers were speaking a rural .... which I couldn't follow.

Vocabulary

8 James suffers from a .... which gets worse when he is nervous.

9 The play was performed in Ancient Greek, but the audience could listen to a .... through headphones.

10 The new president will make his .... in Congress on Wednesday.

M *Complete the sentences with the correct form of one of the following:*

drop	**give**	**make**	**pay**	**raise**
recite	**say**	**state**	**swear**	**tell**

1 He .... his case forcefully.

2 The barrister .... a plea for a light sentence for his client.

3 John .... his word that he would return the money.

4 Maria always .... her prayers before going to bed.

5 The manager .... a hint about my application for the job.

6 Sheila .... several points at the meeting.

7 Juan .... women compliments in a rather old-fashioned way.

8 The witness .... an oath to .... the truth.

9 Pamela will .... her maiden speech in the House of Commons on Thursday.

10 Mary .... the poem perfectly.

N *Select the appropriate word from the following list and put it in the correct sentence.*

squad	**gang**	**unit**	**short list**	**working party**
hit list	**task force**	**brigade**	**night shift**	**quango**

1 The council was short of funds and drew up a .... of services that could easily be cut.

2 The committee set up a .... to report back in a month's time on the feasibility of the proposal.

3 Before knocking off at 8 a.m., the .... explains to men coming on duty any important problems that have arisen with the machinery.

4 In keeping with its view that public accountability is of no importance, the government has set up a new .... to which appointment is by nomination only.

5 Richard looked like a strong candidate for the post but he didn't reach the
....

6 The ...., whose purpose was to establish a secure position, was composed of hardened fighters with considerable war experience.

7 The .... of guards has never had difficulty attracting recruits – it's got far too prestigious a reputation.

8 A .... of young hooligans vandalised the train on which they were returning from an away match.

9 The Vice .... made a swoop on shops in the red-light district and took away a quantity of pornographic material.

10 The Literacy and Basic Skills .... aims to provide help for all those with learning difficulties.

O *In the following exercise, the same adjective is used to qualify two different nouns. What is the opposite of the adjective in each case?*

EXAMPLE: A an old house   *a new house*
                B an old woman   *a young woman*

1 A fine art
   B a fine day
2 A smart clothes
   B a smart student
3 A a plain jumper
   B a plain child
4 A a tough steak
   B a tough job
5 A a generous helping
   B a generous woman

6 A a mild winter
   B a mild cheese
7 A a steep slope
   B a steep price
8 A a wild animal
   B wild flowers
9 A good health
   B good behaviour
10 A fair treatment
    B fair hair

P *Replace the American English expression with its British English equivalent in spelling, vocabulary or grammar. Some sentences contain more than one Americanism.*

1 Would you like a cookie or a candy?

2 Mr Carter's office is on the first floor.

3 She bought a pacifier and some diapers for the baby.

4 Take the elevator to the top floor.

5 We visited New England in the fall.

6 Jeff bought a vest, a necktie and some suspenders.

7 Steve is real good at math.

8 He opened a checking account at the bank.

9 Robert asked his boss for a raise.

10 Susan dove into the water.

Vocabulary

Q *(Follow the instructions in Exercise P)*

1 Lilian washed up before dinner.

2 He explained the administration's defense policy.

3 He wrote a check for new tires.

4 This ice-cream comes in sixty-five flavors.

5 The theater is in the center of town.

6 He used a bullhorn to address the crowd.

7 There was a pitcher of orange juice on the table.

8 At the intersection the sign said 'YIELD'.

9 He filled the bathtub with hot water.

10 The new musical bombed.

R *Complete the sentences with the following idiomatic expressions. You may have to change the form to fit the grammar of the sentence.*

out of the frying-pan into the fire	**stew in his own juice**
touch and go	**look for a needle in a haystack**
split hairs	**egg on his face**
put a brave face on it	**sitting pretty**
skate on thin ice	**he who pays the piper calls the tune**

1 It's John's own fault that he is in all this trouble – let him ....

2 It's a very small distinction – you're just ....

3 The manager's plan is extremely risky – he is certainly ....

4 We will never find it amongst all these papers – it's like ....

5 We are in an extremely advantageous situation – you could say we were
  ....

6 The company is in a precarious financial situation but the chairman is
  ....

7 'I've no idea if we can land safely,' said the pilot as he struggled with the controls. 'It's
  ....'.

8 Since we are providing the funds for this research, we can influence the direction it takes. After all, ...

9 When the new train failed to perform as well as expected, the Chief Engineer had
  ....

10 This is a worse situation than the one we were in before. We have jumped
  ....

S *(Follow the instructions in Exercise* **R***)*

quick on the uptake	**no need to rub it in**
on the off chance	**keep a straight face**
right under your nose	**catch (a person) red-handed**
talk shop	**keep your hand in**
talk to a brick wall	**get a word in edgeways**

1 Conversations with Helen are very one-sided. She talks so fast it's impossible to
....

2 You won't need to explain it to him twice. He's very ....

3 I know I made a terrible mistake. There's ....

4 The police .... the robbers .... as they were trying to break into the bank's vault.

5 Although he had retired from professional tennis, he played regularly in order to
....

6 He went to the theatre box-office .... that there would be tickets for tonight's performance, but there weren't.

7 It's no good trying to persuade him. It's like ....

8 The witness said such amusing things that even the judge could hardly
....

9 I don't know why you couldn't find it yourself. It was ....

10 Since Martin, Bill and Joanna all do the same job, they usually
.... even when they meet socially.

T *Complete the sentences with the following colloquial items:*

come-uppance	**eke out**	**snags**	**kitty**	**nick**
whip-round	**hang**	**perks**	**plonk**	**skives**

1 Everyone in the office contributed £1 a week to the ...., which was used to buy coffee, milk and sugar.

2 Everything went smoothly except for a few .... which we managed to sort out.

3 It is difficult to operate this machine at first, but once you get the .... of it you will find that it saves you a lot of time.

4 It's not very good wine, just a bottle of ....

5 When Christopher left the company, his colleagues had a .... to buy him a present.

6 This job has several ...., including a company car, free lunches and a clothes allowance.

7 John is very lazy and .... off work whenever he has the opportunity.

8 The helicopter lifted the crew off the sinking ship in the .... of time.

9 You can .... this very small amount of meat by mixing it with potatoes.

10 Although I don't like to rejoice when other people suffer, I was really pleased when that tyrannical manager got his ....

Vocabulary

U *Complete the sentences with these compound words:*

spot checks	dry run	dirt cheap	hot potato	cowboy
powder keg	close shave	sandwich course	crash course	ghost writer

1 The smugglers carried out a .... before they actually took any drugs onto the flight.

2 Since he had to learn German in six weeks, he went on a ....

3 There is so much political tension in that part of the world. It's a .... waiting for the spark.

4 The trade union leader said that the strike was being broken by .... lorry drivers.

5 The famous actress employed a .... to help her with her autobiography.

6 Police directed cars into the lay-by to carry out .... on tyres.

7 Why don't you buy some? They are ....

8 Peter's doing a .... at university, so this year he is working for an engineering company.

9 That was a ....! I thought we would never be able to land the aircraft safely.

10 None of the government ministers wanted to take responsibility for the matter, which was generally regarded as a ....

V *In what circumstances, or with reference to what kind of activity, would people make the following remarks?*

1 English or New Zealand?

2 £10 worth of four-star, please.

3 He put it on the 2.30 at Newmarket.

4 Are the colours fast?

5 Matt or gloss?

6 It was a dead heat.

7 They're inside out.

8 Rinse out.

9 I'm not working for peanuts.

10 He's on the box tonight.

W *Complete the gaps in the text with one of the words or phrases provided.*

fringe movement	**acid rain**	**local**
hazards	**emissions**	**inhibit**
lead in petrol	**ecological balance**	**poured**
disposing of waste	**greenhouse effect**	**catastrophic**
fossil fuels	**green movement**	**sea levels**
global warming	**ozone layer**	**trend**
ecological dangers	**damage**	

Environmental pollution is one of the major .... (1)
facing the world in the current decade. The industrialized nations have for years been
burning .... (2) to provide energy as consumer
demand has steadily increased. As Third World countries develop, they are likely to
continue this .... (3) But the .... (4)
from power stations and the burning of wood from forests lead to the build-up of carbon
dioxide in the atmosphere. Carbon dioxide is one of the main gases contributing to
the .... (5) and the destruction of the
.... (6), the layer of atmosphere that protects the
Earth from the effects of harmful rays from the Sun.

The so-called 'greenhouse gases' contribute to .... (7)
and so the melting of the polar ice-caps with a consequent rise in .... (8).
This in turn is likely to lead to potentially .... (9)
effects on low-lying regions such as the delta region of Bangladesh.

But apart from the global aspects of pollution, there are more .... (10)
concerns too. Atmospheric pollution created by noxious fumes from
.... (11) and the pumping of poisonous emissions
from factories into the air is matched in terms of potential danger by the
.... (12) caused to rivers by intensive farming and
the use of these water sources as a means of .... (13). Huge amounts
of nitrogen and phosphorus are .... (14) into rivers,
lakes and seas, and destroy the fragile .... (15).
Both fish and plant life are affected by an environment that can kill all living matter
or provide a favourable environment for the growth of poisonous algae that in turn
.... (16) other animal and plant life.

.... (17) is also an important factor in the state of
rivers, though one of its major effects is on forests. Trees are adversely affected by the
acid content of the rain and begin to wither and die. In the light of such serious known
effects, it comes as no surprise to see the growth of a .... (18), both in
politics and consumerism, as the general public becomes more conscious of the
.... (19) posed by daily life. The green movement has
moved on from its 1970's and 1980's position as a .... (20)
supported mainly by cranks, to a major force in conscience-raising for politicians and
the public at large.

Vocabulary

X *Complete the gaps in the text with one of the words or phrases provided.*

mugged	redundancy	congested	rush hour	pressure
on the dole	picked	affluence	traffic jams	graffiti
inner-city	stressful	vandalism	tube	high-rise

Cities towards the end of the twentieth century are very .... (1)
places to live. As always, there is .... (2) caused when vast
numbers of people live in a limited area. There are perpetual .... (3),
even outside the .... (4), as the streets are heavily
.... (5) with too much traffic. If you travel on the
.... (6), there is the danger of being
.... (7) or of having your pocket
.... (8). There are signs of .... (9)
all around, from the .... (10) written on the walls to the
litter and broken glass at your feet. As those with jobs go off to work, those
.... (11) get through the day as best they can. Not for them
worries about what the boss says or threats of .... (12) or
looking forward to some relaxation at the weekend. Weekends are the same as weekdays,
as they observe their urban landscape of .... (13) buildings
in the .... (14), with no hope of escape to the
.... (15) of suburbs and countryside.

Y *Complete the gaps in the text with one of the words or phrases provided.*

funded	adapt their skills	access
achieve their potential	on-the-job	elite
enter the labour market	national curriculum	loan
skilled personnel	private education	tertiary
primary education	training the mind	secondary
vocational education	drop-out	entitled

Education is a subject that is of great concern to parents, children and politicians alike.
What systems provide the young with the best chance to .... (1)?
What systems are fairest in terms of .... (2) for those
from rich and poor backgrounds? Should children be educated for the jobs likely to be
available when they leave school or should they be given a general training that will
allow them to .... (3) to any type of job that becomes
available? Should there be a .... (4), or should there
be local variation according to the needs of the particular pupils?

Every society has its own answer to questions such as these, but in most countries in
the industrialised world, education is divided into .... (5),
from the age of 5 to 11, ... (6) from 11 to 16 (or
whenever the country fixes the school-leaving age) and .... (7),
i.e. post school. The division between .... (8)
(training for jobs) and academic education (.. (9))

is one that is hotly debated, and the need for technical training in schools is also a subject for discussion. While the majority of parents decide on state education, which is free in many countries, a number opt for .... (10), often a costly business, and one associated with particular religious groups in some countries.

University education varies greatly from country to country, both in the number of students .... (11) to enter the system, in how they have to pay (i.e. are they .... (12) through a grant or through a .... (13) that has to be repaid) and in the length of courses. Countries that provide access to a large percentage of school-leavers often have a high .... (14) rate as those who find the pressure of completing their studies too much give up and .... (15). Every industrialised country has a need of .... (16), but it is not clear whether the skills required are best developed through state education or .... (17) training. There is also the question of whether higher education should be available to all or limited to a narrow .... (18).

Z *Complete the gaps in the text with one of the words or phrases provided.*

coalition	polling booth	counted
universal suffrage	democracy	voter
cast their vote	constituency	majority
proportional representation	secret ballot	elections
an overall majority	ballot paper	alliance
minority groups	goes to the polls	express

Political systems in Europe are characterised by the idea of .... (1). A key feature of these systems is the need to hold .... (2) at regular intervals, to enable the population to .... (3) its political wishes by electing a parliament. .... (4) means that, in most of the countries under discussion at least, all men and women over the age of .... (5) (with the exception of special groups such as the military or the prison population) have the right to .... (6) in support of the party or candidate of their choice. Voting is by means of a .... (7), and on election day, when the country .... (8), each .... (9) goes to a polling station. There a .... (10) will be supplied and each voter records a vote for the candidate(s) of their choice. It is a key element of the system that the voter should be able to cast his vote in the privacy of a .... (11), and to be able to mark the ballot paper with the name of his choice without observation or interference. When the polls close, the votes are .... (12).

Vocabulary

In Britain, the candidate with the highest number of votes is elected as the member of parliament for a given .... (13). This system, known as the 'first past the post system', is in contrast to that of .... (14), which allows a number of seats in the parliament for a particular party proportional to the percentage of the vote received. This system allows .... (15) to have a greater say in parliament and also leads to more .... (16) government, where parties whose political views and aims are different may join together to form a government because no one party has achieved .... (17). Each party will then have to compromise on its political programme and concentrate on what can actually be achieved by an .... (18) with other parties.

Phrasal Verbs

A *Complete the following sentences using a phrasal verb with* **give**. *You may have to use some verbs more than once.*

1 You never know what Ben is thinking. He doesn't .... anything ....

2 When children in the area started to suffer from serious illnesses, their mothers blamed a local factory where the tall chimney .... fumes.

3 I've no idea what the answer is. I .... Tell me.

4 The wrestler won the contest because his opponent ....

5 This is a lovely room. As you can see, it .... the rose garden.

6 Sam was forced to .... his job in the City because of ill health.

7 David enjoys borrowing books, but frequently forgets to .... them ....

8 It was a difficult decision but Maria knew it was best to .... her boyfriend rather than face opposition from both families.

9 A log fire .... plenty of heat.

10 Daniel wanted to lose weight but wasn't too keen on the idea of .... eating lots of the things he liked best.

B *Complete the following sentences using a phrasal verb with* **put**. *You may have to use some verbs more than once.*

1 I don't believe for a minute that Suzie is really ill. If you ask me, she's just .... it ....

2 Because of heavy snowfalls in the region we have had to .... the meeting of the Conservation Group.

3 The plan .... by the council didn't meet with the approval of the electorate.

4 At least five people have .... the job in Accounts.

5 I just had to move out of my flat. I couldn't .... the noise from the road any more.

6 The school drama society has decided to .... *Richard III*.

7 It's expensive staying in a hotel in London. Isn't there anyone who could .... you ....?

8 Please remember to .... the lights when you leave the room.

9 The Sales Director .... it .... that the Finance Department was being badly run.

10 Richard and Anne wanted to go climbing but the bad weather .... them ....

59

Phrasal Verbs

C *Complete the following sentences using a phrasal verb with* **do**. *You may have to use some verbs more than once.*

1 I'm worn out. I could .... a cup of tea.

2 Robert has just bought a run-down old cottage and is looking forward to .... it ....

3 Jennifer was going to have an operation in the afternoon, so she had to .... lunch.

4 John's not at all popular, perhaps because he's always .... his colleagues.

5 With the introduction of computers, a lot of firms have begun to .... outmoded clerical systems.

6 Harry was .... a fortune when his accountant tricked him into investing in a shady business in which he himself had an interest.

7 A twenty-mile hike is enough to make anyone feel ....

8 A cold wind was blowing so Andrew told the children to .... their coats.

9 Thomas is so naughty I just don't know what to .... him.

10 'The bullet got Harry,' said the soldier. 'He's ....'

D *Complete the following sentences using a phrasal verb with* **make**. *You may have to use some verbs more than once.*

1 When questioned by the police about her whereabouts on the night of the crime, the suspect .... that she had been with a boyfriend.

2 You've known Paul for a week now. What do you .... him?

3 It's always easier to start a quarrel than to .... after it.

4 The adventurer was .... the North Pole when bad weather made it necessary to turn back.

5 The muggers attacked the pensioner and .... with her money.

6 After twenty days out of sight of land, the ship's captain thought he could .... an island on the horizon.

7 The actor was .... his face before the performance.

8 I'm sorry I forgot your birthday. Let's go out on Saturday, and I'll .... it .... to you, I promise.

9 How did you .... on your trip to South America?

10 The lawyer couldn't .... whether her client was telling the truth.

E *Complete the following sentences using a phrasal verb with* **fall**. *You may have to use some verbs more than once.*

1 Paul was ill in hospital for ten weeks and so he .... with his school work.

2 As the longest-serving employee in the company, it .... me to make the speech wishing our office manager well in his retirement.

3 It is not a successful group. They don't get on with one another and .... over the slightest thing.

4 Sales of the electric car were buoyant in the last quarter of the year but they have .... this spring.

5 Don't make any special arrangements for me. I'll .... with what other people want.

6 I should be in Italy now but my holiday plans .... when the travel company went bust.

7 The wall .... when heavy rain caused the ground to move.

8 Mary made a good effort in the test but .... on the last question.

9 There was no fence around the pool and a number of children ....

10 Jane and Shelley .... with each other when it came to determining what each should contribute to the household budget.

F *Complete the following sentences using a phrasal verb with* **pick**. *You may have to use some verbs more than once.*

1 Frank never studied German. He just .... it .... on holiday in Germany.

2 Tom's a bully. He always .... boys younger and smaller than he is.

3 Anna wasn't feeling well, and it was obvious to her friends from the way she just .... her dinner.

4 Sales were poor last year, but with the improving economic situation this year, we expect them to .... considerably.

5 The idea in identification parades is that a witness will .... the person responsible for the crime from a group of specially selected people.

6 It had been a long day. Helen .... her papers, put them in her briefcase and left the office.

7 The sniper positioned himself at the window and was ready to .... any soldier who attempted to get across the street.

8 Janet was quite ill after the operation but is beginning to .... now.

9 The old steam engine laboured up the hill but .... speed on the descent.

10 The music teacher had an uncanny knack of being able to .... those pupils with promise after they had played just a few bars.

Phrasal Verbs

G *Complete the following sentences using a phrasal verb (or a noun derived from one) with* **take**. *You may have to use some verbs more than once.*

1 He decided to .... a life insurance policy.

2 Mrs Brown no longer .... lodgers.

3 He was .... when he saw the extent of the damage to his orchard.

4 You'll have to move these filing cabinets. They .... too much space.

5 I explained the plan but I don't think he .... it ....

6 As far as her behaviour is concerned she really .... her father.

7 I don't feel like cooking tonight. Let's get a Chinese ....

8 This patient's .... of carbohydrates is very low.

9 You are not obliged to say anything, but anything you do say will be .... and may be used in evidence against you.

10 Running a marathon really .... it .... of you.

H *Complete the following sentences using a phrasal verb with* **turn**. *You may have to use some verbs more than once.*

1 Life very rarely .... as you expect.

2 Chris was offered an interesting post in the north of England but she had to .... it .... when her husband refused to move there.

3 A number of fans were .... from the concert because there were no more tickets left.

4 If you don't pay your rent you can expect to be .... of your flat.

5 Charlotte certainly knows when it pays to .... the charm.

6 We were cold so we .... the central heating to 70 degrees.

7 If you hadn't been teasing the dog, it wouldn't have .... you.

8 People who live alone often feel they have no one to .... in case of emergency.

9 If you don't want the neighbours to complain, you'd better .... your stereo.

10 Archaeologists excavating the Bronze Age site have .... some very interesting remains.

I *Complete the following sentences using a phrasal verb with* **keep**. *You may have to use some verbs more than once.*

1 Danger. ....

2 The number of deer in the woods is .... by the gamekeeper who culls the aged animals each autumn.

3 Sam makes a lot of effort but he finds it hard to .... with the most talented members of the group.

4 Although Shirley gave up studying the piano at the age of eighteen, she still .... it .... and performs for family occasions.

5 Don't accuse Hugh of cheating. He always .... the rules.

6 Although Caroline and John have lived abroad for ten years, they still manage to .... with their friends' news through a regular exchange of letters.

7 In learning a language, it's infuriating how easy it is to .... making the same grammatical mistakes.

8 Mark has all the makings of a politician. He certainly knows how to .... the people that matter.

9 The supervisor .... at the staff to improve their performance until they were sick of hearing the same thing.

10 Although the interviewer tried hard to get the answers to searching questions, the politician always managed to .... something ....

J *Complete the sentences using a phrasal verb with* **hold**. *You may need to use some verbs more than once.*

1 .... please while I see if Mr Smith is in his office.

2 His boss always .... it .... David that he had criticised his marketing strategy in front of senior staff.

3 Four armed men .... a security guard as he came out of the bank carrying two bags full of used notes.

4 The staff didn't .... a soft approach to discipline.

5 Despite his illness, he managed to .... a very demanding job.

6 After twenty-one days no hope was .... for earthquake victims buried underground.

7 A strike at the ports .... export orders for two months.

8 The fort was surrounded but the garrison .... the attack for more than twenty-four hours.

9 The management side made an improved pay offer but the unions decided to .... for the original demand of 12%.

10 Furious, Marianne managed, with difficulty, to .... her anger.

Phrasal Verbs

K *Complete each sentence using a phrasal verb with* **clear**. *You may need to use some verbs more than once.*

1 There was a lot of fog this morning but now it is .... and the sun is shining.

2 When everyone at the table had finished eating, the plates were ....

3 Mary developed a bad rash on her hands after using that detergent, but it .... when she used the ointment the doctor prescribed.

4 Why don't you just .... and leave me alone?

5 There seems to have been some sort of misunderstanding about the Smiths' bill. Could you help me to .... the matter ....?

6 It's always fun to have a party, but .... afterwards is a big chore.

7 It was time I .... those cupboards. Just look at all the stuff I've got for the next jumble sale.

8 As soon as the weather .... the climbers resumed their attempt on the summit.

9 Your study looks a total mess. Don't you ever think of .... it ....?

10 By working overtime every week, Alice was able to .... the debt within six months.

L *Complete each sentence using a phrasal verb with* **drop**. *You may need to use a verb more than once.*

1 We were feeling a bit fed up after an awful day at work, so we decided to .... for a drink at the pub before setting off for home.

2 John found it so comfortable in his first-class seat on the train from London to Bristol that he couldn't stop himself .... He only woke up when the train got to the station.

3 Teenagers who .... of school often find it hard to gain qualifications later.

4 The home help promised to .... the shopping .... on her way home.

5 Virginia Smith had to .... of the competition because the horse she was riding injured its leg.

6 Sales of petrol .... when the government increased the tax by 50%.

7 The runner made a great start to the race but .... during the last lap.

8 George .... with his studies when he started to play football seriously and the crunch came when he had to revise for his exams.

9 Guess who .... when you were out.

10 Interest in the project .... sharply when it became clear there was inadequate funding for it to be fully successful.

M *Complete the following sentences using a phrasal verb with* **stand**. *You may need to use some verbs more than once.*

1 What do the letters I.M.F. ....?

2 Everyone .... after the accident feeling helpless, just waiting for the police and ambulance.

3 Robert, I just can't make the meeting tomorrow. If I give you all the details, could you .... me.

4 The plane is on the runway, ... for take-off.

5 This time you've gone too far. I won't .... such behaviour. I'm going to report you to the boss.

6 I've never understood in detail what the Green Party ....

7 Paul Simmons put himself forward as a candidate in the presidential elections, but after a poor showing at the polls, he was forced to ....

8 If you don't .... your rights, you will soon lose them.

9 Amongst a group of very talented musicians, this competitor .... as being quite exceptional.

10 Women in the borough are being encouraged to attend self-defence classes to teach them how to .... their attackers.

N *Complete the following sentences using a phrasal verb with* **come**. *You may need to use some verbs more than once.*

1 I know Frank doesn't agree with you about going to Spain on holiday, but if you try hard to persuade him, he's sure to .... your way of thinking.

2 How did it .... that you went to university in Edinburgh?

3 Darling, I'm afraid I'll be home late tonight. Something's .... at work.

4 Doctor, I'm worried about Sam. He's .... in spots.

5 Caroline expects to .... quite a lot of money when her aunt dies.

6 Steve was knocked unconscious when he fell off his motorbike and didn't .... for several minutes.

7 .... it! I don't believe for a moment that you're serious about getting a job in Australia.

8 Where's the price tag for this dress? It must have ....

9 Don't stand there on the doorstep. ....!

10 ....! I can't spend all day waiting for you.

Phrasal Verbs

O *Complete the following sentences with a word in the list.*

ease off	bowled over	brought down	whisked away	picked up
gone down with	soldier on	crack down	phased out	warm-up

1 When Jay Doncaster, the pop star, arrived at London Airport, he gave a press conference and was then .... to a secret destination in the capital.

2 If you are thinking of going jogging, it's always essential to do some .... exercises first.

3 It's pouring. Let's wait for the rain to .... before we go shopping.

4 Andy's .... flu and won't be able to attend the meeting.

5 The regime's economic problems caused it to be ....

6 Out-of-date computers will be .... in schools to allow updated models to be introduced.

7 The sight of his bride in her wedding dress just .... Tom ....

8 The police decided to .... on drug offenders, and staged a number of early morning raids.

9 Despite having had two heart attacks, Jack decided to .... at work until he reached retirement age.

10 Martin .... a virus on a trip to Europe and is now gravely ill.

P *Complete the following sentences with a word in the list.*

wear off	run out of	passed over	clued up	knocked out
pass up	fall-out	called up	cooling off	call-out

1 At the Wimbledon Tennis Championship, the reigning champion was .... in the first round.

2 If you want to know anything about computers, ask Richard. He's very ....

3 Oh dear! We've .... tonic water. I'll have to have soda instead.

4 Nuclear .... is a major hazard in the event of an accident at a nuclear power station.

5 John was .... for promotion so he decided to leave the company.

6 I hate having injections at the dentist's. They always take ages to .... afterwards.

7 In disputes between management and trade unions, it's a good idea to allow a .... period.

8 Don't .... the chance of visiting Disney World.

9 Until 1958, young men of 18 in the UK were .... for military service.

10 If you need a plumber during a Bank Holiday weekend, don't forget that there's a £50 minimum .... charge.

Q *Complete the following sentences with a word in the list.*

shoot-out	make-up	get-up	turn-out	sell-out
stand-in	put-down	take-over	take-off	getaway

1 The plane crashed immediately after ....

2 The .... at the meeting was most satisfactory. Nearly a hundred people came.

3 After the .... of British Caledonian by British Airways, new contracts were issued to the staff.

4 Louise wanted tickets for the Madonna concert but couldn't get any. It was a .... on the first day tickets were available.

5 The thieves made their .... in a stolen car.

6 The soldiers surrounded the house where the terrorists were holding hostages, and in the .... that followed, two people were killed.

7 'I thought we were going to see Anthony Hopkins in this play.' 'Yes, but he's ill. That's his ....'

8 The fashion in .... this year is for green eye-shadow.

9 The twins appeared at their mother's party in the strangest ....

10 Michael regarded it as a .... when his boss chose someone else to be in charge of Sales Promotion.

R *Complete the sentences with a word in the list.*

over and done with	worn out	fed up	stand-by	tied up
put out	tired out	done for	cut out for	burnt out

1 It's no good expecting May to smile. She's always thoroughly ....

2 I don't know what flight I'll be coming by. I'm travelling on a .... ticket.

3 No, I'm afraid you can't speak to Mr Smith. He's .... at a meeting.

4 Shirley was most .... when her fiancé said he was going on holiday without her.

5 I'll have to get some new shoes. These are quite ....

6 John was .... That's why he went to bed at 8 o'clock.

7 I've resigned. I'm just not .... a career in selling.

8 The past is .... Let's make a new start.

9 In the City many people are .... by the age of thirty.

10 When the mine exploded under the politician's car, we knew he was ....

Phrasal Verbs

S *Rewrite the sentences, using a phrasal verb that means the opposite of the words in italics. Make any additional changes that may be necessary.*

EXAMPLE: Andy *went to bed* early.
Andy got up early.

1   Alexander *fell asleep* at ten o'clock.

2   Those houses *were built* in 1950.

3   The plane will *land* in ten minutes.

4   Henry *put on* his jacket.

5   Charles and Anna have *started going out together*.

6   The company has *taken on* two hundred workers.

7   Maria's parents *disliked* her boyfriend the moment they met him.

8   The nurse was there when Alastair *lost consciousness*.

9   Jan *gave up* jogging last summer.

10   Sam *left* the party at midnight.

Correct Verb Forms

A *In the following sentences, put the verbs in the correct form.*

1 Teresa (type) all day and still not (finish) the report.

2 Doctor, I (get) lots of aches and pains. (Be) anything wrong? I (be) terribly worried.

3 John just (complete) a course in engineering and now (want) pursue his studies by (take) a Master's degree.

4 For some years now Samantha (believe) strongly in reincarnation and (try) to persuade her friends to come round to her way of thinking but they (be) still not convinced.

5 Martha (think) of going on a three-month trip to Mexico next year and (wonder) for some time if any of her fellow students (like) (accompany) her.

6 While Thomas (spend) the last few months working hard at his studies, his sisters (concentrate) their attention on how to get their new business off the ground.

7 It (look) as if oil (leak) from this pipe for some time. We (have) to dismantle the machine if it (be) (be put right).

8 I not (want) to go to the supermarket again at the moment. I (prefer) to wait till the end of the month, when I (can) do all the shopping in one go.

9 'You (go) to the Tower of London?'
   'No, not yet. I (want) to go ever since I arrived in London, but something always (come) up. I (hope) (go) sometime soon. Perhaps you (like) (come) with me?'

10 The constant humming from the word-processor (give) me a headache. I (have) to take an aspirin.

B *Put the verbs in the correct form.*

1 This candidate (look) very promising. Just think about his experience. He (live) in Hong Kong, Australia and the USA and (work) for a number of multi-national companies. I (think) we definitely (interview) him.

2 There (be) a terrible storm last month and several trees (fall down). The telephone lines (bring down) and some still not (be fixed). Roads (be blocked) for several hours. Several homes (suffer) damage to their roofs and chimneys that (be) very expensive to repair.

3 I asked Tom last week to find out this information, but he still not (do) so. I (have) (ask) him again.

4 Marianna (complain) about her husband for ages. I not (be) surprised that he (leave) her. What she (do) now, on her own?

5 I (try) for ages to reach you. Where you (be)?

6 Someone (try) get in through the kitchen window during the night. If you (look) carefully, you (be able) see the marks.

7 The police (question) the suspect for several hours, but so far they not (get) any new information from him.

8 Everyone (be) excited about the news of the wedding and (think) about what they (wear) on the big day next month.

9 The flood water (breach) the new dam and villagers now (flee) from the flood.

10 News from the earthquake zone (be) that over two hundred people (be) injured. Help (be) urgently required.

C *Put the verbs in the correct form.*

1 'How many times Stephen (telephone)?' 'I not (know), but I wish he (stop). It's such a bore when he keeps on (phone).'

2 If you (be) president of the country, what changes you (want) introduce?

3 I wish I not (eat) so many cakes. They (make) me feel quite ill.

4 Martin (be) here now if he (allow) plenty of time for the journey. As it (be), we (have) to start the meeting without him.

5 Mary (agree) to the conditions laid down by the court yesterday provided that her husband (keep) to his side of the bargain.

6 I not (believe) what you (say) about Anna. She never (lie) to anyone, least of all to me about such an important matter.

7 If only I (realise) you (come) to England this week, I (keep) my diary free. As it (be), I (be) afraid it (be) just impossible to meet unless you (come) to Oxford on Tuesday evening.

8 Supposing the company (offer) you a pay rise of 50%, (be) you so determined to leave and look for a job elsewhere?

9 'How you (feel) when you (receive) the offer?' 'Like everyone, I (be) delighted. You not (be)?'

10 Helena (think) (set up) her own business. What advice you (give) her?

D *Put the verbs in the correct form.*

1 What you (mean), the accident (be) my fault? If it (be), surely I not (call) the police.

2 If John (telephone) you last night and (invite) you to dinner, what you (do)?

3 It not (be) possible for me attend the meeting yesterday, if my deputy not (agree) (stand in) for me at short notice.

4 Basil certainly not (get) through the interview so successfully if Jim not (spend) a lot of time (prepare) him about what to say.

5 I wish I (speak) Swedish. If I (can), I (understand) the film we (see) last night much better.

6 The bank account not (overdraw) at the end of last month if you not (write) a cheque (pay) for the new washing machine.

7 It (be) hot in this room, and the lecturer (be) very boring. I wish I (lie) on the beach, (enjoy) the sun and (listen) to the waves.

8 I quite (agree) with you. Rupert (be) a good worker, I not (say) he not (be). I just wish he (co-operate) more with other people.

9 I (go) to see the film last night but at the last minute I (receive) an important phone-call and (have) to stay at home to finish some urgent work. I not (regret) it. I (hear) since from my friends who (go) that it not (be) very good.

10 Ruth (regret) (be) rude to Simon. The atmosphere between them (be) now very tense, and she (like) make things up. He not (help) by (be) very distant.

E *Put the verbs in the correct form, using appropriate modal verbs as necessary.*

1 I wish the central heating not (keep) (play up). It (be) a bore not (know) from one day to the next if it (work) or not.

2 This chicken (taste) better if the chef (add) a little more seasoning.

3 If only it not (rain), then I (be able) to plant the seedlings today.

4 Tim not (regret) (spend) money on (modernise) the house if he (get) his money back when he (sell) it.

5 I (go) to the party but for the fact that my youngest son (have) a temperature and I not (want) leave him. Just as well, as it (turn) out, because when the doctor (come) he decided Stephen (admit) to hospital.

6 'Where's Joan? She (say) she (be) at the station at 3, and now it's 3.15. She must (miss) the train. I (hope) she not (miss) the next one, otherwise we (be) late for the opening address at the conference.'

7 'What you (do) when the course (finish)?' 'I not (know) yet. Perhaps I (have) a holiday first and then (look) for a job.'

8 I not (ask) you such an embarrassing question here in front of other people if I not (feel) it necessary to get at the truth.

9 'What you (do) if the police realise you (give) them false information?' 'I just (say) I (be) mistaken.'

10 By the time Julius (read) my letter telling him it's all over between us, I (be) hundreds of miles away, sunning myself on a tropical beach, only wishing I (leave) him sooner.

Correct Verb Forms

F *Put the verbs in the correct form.*

1 If John (ask) where I (go), tell him I (be) back as soon as I possibly (can). He (need) not worry, it not (be) later than Thursday.

2 When the President (step) off the plane on his official visit to our country next week, he (greet) by the Prime Minister and the Defence Minister. He then (drive) to the Prime Minister's official residence where a State Reception (take) place in his honour. The moment that (be) over, he (take) to Worcester Castle where he (spend) the night.

3 I (tell) John the whole story about my early life, but the fact that he (be) so unsympathetic about the first details I revealed (make) me decide not to.

4 I not (realise) that Stella (pass) the exam the last time it was conducted. If I (know), I not (insist) on her filling in another form.

5 I (realise) I not (understand) the question when the interpreter (repeat) it slowly in my own language.

6 (Be) it not for Mary's help, I not (be able) to take part in the competition. As it (be), I (manage) to win first prize, so I (be) eternally indebted to her.

7 When the school finally (close) its doors in 1988, Mr Roberts (teach) there for 25 years. As a result of the closure, he (decide) to take early retirement and (be) now to be seen tending his garden most sunny afternoons.

8 Consultations (take) place for many years at the highest level before concrete peace proposals (accept).

9 Leading a life of luxury on the Costa del Sol (become) a reality for many fugitives from British justice in the 1980's.

10 The financial scandal (rock) the government when many senior politicians (see) to be implicated and (force) (resign).

G *Put the verbs in the correct form, using appropriate modal verbs when necessary.*

1 You must (be) very pleased when you (hear) you (win) the prize. What you (do) to celebrate?

2 I (try) (get) John on the phone for the past week. I think he must (go) abroad. You (have) any idea when he (be) back?

3 I not (need) (tell) Alison the bad news. She already (hear). Chris (tell) her the previous evening.

4 I really ought (let) the college know where they (can) contact me in case of emergency during the vacation. If I (have), they not (need) (get) in touch with the local police.

5 Oh, Martin. What a lovely bunch of flowers you (give) me. How very kind of you. But really, you (do).

6 The interviewer not (dare) ask the Minister the questions he really (want) to. The atmosphere (be) too threatening.

7 Sam (offer) a new job. He not (be able) (decide) if he (take) it or not. He (have) (let) them (know) by the end of the week.

8 I (spend) ages (make) preparations for the dinner party but I not (need) (bother). At the last moment, Philip (ring) (say) he not (be able) (come).

9 (Be) you sure the answer (be) what it (be)? In my opinion, it not (be) right. Surely you (forget) (include) something essential?

10 I (have) a day off last week. I just (dare) not ask my boss for another day off tomorrow.

Key

Articles, Quantifiers and their Compounds

A

1 an	6 an	11 a	16 an
2 an	7 an	12 a	17 an
3 an	8 an	13 an	18 a
4 an	9 a	14 an	19 an
5 a	10 a	15 a	20 a

B
1 the violin
2 *correct*
3 the Oxford road
4 *correct*
5 *correct*
6 *correct*
7 the summer; the Alps
8 the prison
9 the home
10 *correct*

C
1 any
2 any
3 some
4 any
5 any/some
6 some
7 any
8 any
9 any
10 any/some

D
1 some
2 some
3 some
4 any
5 any
6 any
7 any
8 any
9 some
10 some

E
1 anywhere
2 sometime
3 anything/ something
4 anywhere
5 anyone
6 any time
7 sometime
8 somehow
9 some time
10 somewhere

F
1 someone
2 nothing
3 any more
4 anything
5 any more
6 some time
7 anything
8 nothing
9 anything
10 someone

G
eggs 1,2,3,4,6,8,9,10
luggage 3,4,5,6,8
questions 1,2,3,4,6,8,9,10
furniture 3,4,5,6,8
enquiries 1,2,3,4,6,8,9,10
money 3,4,5,6,8
advice 3,4,5,6,8
news 3,4,5,6,8
progress 3,4,5,6,8

H
clothes 1,2,3,5,6,9
hair 1,2,4,5,6,7,10
laugh 4,7
experience 1,2,4,5,6,7,10
laughter 1,2,4,5,6,10
police 1,2,3,5,6
intelligence 1,2,4,5,6,10
strength 1,2,4,5,6,10
book 4,5,7

Note: *A little laugh* and *a little book* are, of course, only possible for different reasons from those which allow No. 4 to combine with other items in the list. *Intelligence* and *strength* may be preceded directly by *all* (No. 6) or, more commonly, *all her/your/their*, etc.

Verb Tenses (active and passive)

A
1 is; are saying
2 am looking; Do you know; is; is; know; is
3 am trying; is; are making; Do you think
4 believe; is; is trying; wants
5 are being; is getting
6 is making; spends
7 tidy up; leave
8 is always criticising; do
9 am dying
10 is leaking; are closing off

B
1 will not be; is promoted
2 sets; will be suffused
3 I'll; get
4 predict/are predicting; comes
5 finishes/has finished; will be
6 will be/is; appears
7 have; will go ahead
8 will be; reach
9 get; will be able
10 signs; will need; is

C
1 have visited
2 was; knew
3 have ever tasted
4 has lived and worked; has been living and working
5 lived
6 have already read
7 worked; completed
8 has passed
9 have known; have never understood; attracted
10 have never been; heard

73

D
1 was living; met; became
2 heard; wanted; was; invited
3 hit; were having
4 could; was going
5 was; was blowing
6 was, could; did; got; was; did not start; wanted
7 was just striking; came
8 was not; was travelling
9 did not ride; was; announced; was expecting
10 was; was shining; were singing; looked/was looking

E
1 have loved
2 have always wanted
3 have I been asked
4 have been having
5 has been having
6 have you been studying
7 have been trying; have you been
8 has been going
9 has taken
10 has been sleeping

F
1 graduated; spent; was offered; wanted
2 had been looking; met; fell
3 had known; was; went
4 had; was; had been working
5 looked; had put/put
6 had been circulating; was made
7 had been receiving/had received; was finally told; had been cured
8 began; read/had read
9 didn't you go; thought; liked; had already seen; went; was
10 weren't you; was not told/hadn't been told

G
1 didn't you
2 aren't I
3 oughtn't they
4 mustn't she
5 hadn't you
6 wouldn't you
7 mightn't it
8 could it
9 is it
10 isn't it
11 won't it
12 would he
13 shall we
14 will you
15 could he
16 will you
17 did they
18 won't you
19 will they
20 was there

H
1 All the pipes must be checked for leaks.
2 An increased dividend was announced.
3 The complaint will be thoroughly investigated.
4 The place where the treasure was buried was not known.
5 The police might have been informed.
6 The cracks in the side of the fuselage had not been noticed.
7 The truth would never have been known if . . .
8 If his true identity had been realised, he would have been arrested.
9 Was anything important discussed?
10 A safety helmet has to be worn on the site.

I
1 These premises are patrolled by guards every day.
2 The X-rays are being studied by the doctor.
3 The car will be repaired by the mechanic tomorrow.
4 Seven apple trees have been planted by Martin, our new gardener.
5 Nothing of any real value was taken by the burglars.
6 The tomb had been opened by robbers long before it was found by archaeologists.
7 The drugs were being transferred from one car to another by the smugglers when the police arrived.
8 Lord Fauntleroy's country-house is going to be designed by a famous architect.
9 A minimum fine of £100 must be paid by motorists convicted of speeding.
10 The annual government subsidy might be lost by the museum.

J
1 I was told that the best way to get marks off my trousers was to have them cleaned.
2 It was a shock for everyone when news of the disaster was announced.
3 The law of gravity was formulated by Newton.
4 Judith left the house under the cover of darkness so as not to be seen/so that she would not be seen.
5 Details of the secret meeting with representatives of the terrorist organisation were revealed by an aide to the minister.
6 James is said to be the most gifted mathematician ever produced by the department.
7 If the accused had been found guilty he would surely have been given a prison sentence.
8 This sweater must be washed by hand.
9 Passengers travelling by air are advised to wear comfortable clothing during long flights.
10 Satellite dishes are being produced at the rate of 500 a week, but they are selling slowly.

74

K
1. be converted; are provided
2. to be felt
3. are shown; are not allowed
4. is currently being decommissioned; will not be finished
5. was dressed up; had been invited
6. were damaged; were made/had been made
7. will have been built
8. are asked; are given/have been given; be rectified
9. are now being conducted; to be used
10. has never been established

Gerunds and Infinitives

A
1. to eat
2. Smoking
3. talking
4. to do
5. adjusting
6. having
7. to win
8. turning
9. behaving
10. to be

B
1. living; living/to live
2. ringing
3. wasting
4. to inform
5. avoiding
6. to lie
7. to think
8. going
9. Gardening
10. to admit

C
1. speaking
2. retaliate
3. winning
4. living
5. talking
6. meet
7. help
8. turn
9. cutting
10. go; stay

D
1. reaching
2. succeed
3. looking; helping
4. handling
5. creating
6. apply
7. tell
8. receive
9. undertake
10. help

E
1. I don't approve of Harry and Sally('s) sharing a flat in the centre of the city.
2. I don't like Peter('s) coming home late.
3. John's delighted at being promoted/having been promoted.
4. It's the fact of the house being on the main road that makes it difficult to sell.
5. Employees are put out at being paid late.
6. I was woken up by the baby('s) crying.
7. Anna's mother was annoyed at Anna('s) dropping the plate.
8. Buying a new house is always expensive.
9. Wearing jeans is not allowed in this disco.
10. Andrew, congratulations on winning/ having won the competition.

F
1. John is responsible for handling orders for new stock.
2. I don't believe my grandfather is capable of committing a crime.
3. Amelia is proud of passing/having passed her driving-test first time.
4. Jane apologised for being late.
5. We suspect the girl's father of murdering/ having murdered her.
6. This area is well-known for producing excellent beef.
7. Charles is interested in collecting first editions of twentieth-century authors.
8. I'm annoyed at Jake for spending/having spent so much money on a new set of golf-clubs.
9. I'm used to living alone.
10. Harriet is fonder of playing tennis than going sailing.

G to think; doing; to maintain; to do; (to) move; moving; leaving; to have/having; to do; being told/to be told; saying/say; do; doing; to come; living.

H
1. Within twenty-four hours of being released from prison, he had committed further offences.
2. After being examined by a specialist, he agreed to be operated on.
3. I am looking forward to going to the ball and being introduced to the prince.
4. The water-level is to be checked every day as long as the drought continues.
5. These new regulations are to be followed at all times.
6. The manager was in favour of new machinery being purchased.
7. These patrols are likely to be ambushed before they get anywhere near their objective.
8. He was very anxious about being interviewed.
9. The injured climbers had to be lifted off the mountain by helicopter.
10. The manuscript is believed to have been forged in the early nineteenth century.

Conditionals

A
1. If the weather is all right we'll go abseiling on Sunday.
2. Tony would show more interest in his schoolwork if his parents encouraged him.
3. If I entered the competition, I might win.

4 It'll only take you ten minutes to walk to the house if you take the short cut across the park.

5 Sally wouldn't keep getting colds if she looked after herself.

6 If Robert doesn't stop working so hard/If Robert carries on working far too hard he'll give himself a heart attack.

7 If there is a severe storm tonight, the roof will leak/the rain will come through the hole in the roof.

8 If you don't keep the kitchen spotless, it can be a major source of infection.

9 You'd better run if you want to catch the train./If you run you may catch the train./You'll miss the train if you don't run.

10 If I were you, I'd make a clean breast of it.

B 1 If Martin had set his alarm, he wouldn't have woken up late.

2 The milk wouldn't have gone off if Tom hadn't left it out of the fridge.

3 If Alison had been promoted she wouldn't have resigned.

4 If Chris had had enough money for the bus fare, he wouldn't have had to walk home/he would have caught the bus.

5 The climbers wouldn't have been stranded if the weather hadn't deteriorated suddenly before they reached the summit.

6 The injured climber wouldn't have been rescued if the helicopter hadn't spotted him.

7 John wouldn't have lost everything he had if he hadn't invested all his savings in one company, which then went into liquidation.

8 The sales force wouldn't have been able to achieve the target they had been set if they hadn't made/without making a huge effort.

9 If the crew hadn't acted swiftly in lowering the emergency chute, the passengers would not all have escaped.

10 There wouldn't have been a teacher shortage if there had been sufficient/adequate planning on the part of the authorities.
   Note: Other possible correct answers exist, particularly if the vocabulary is changed, e.g. for No. 2 .... *if Tom had put it back in the fridge.*

C 1 If it hadn't been for the presence of/If there hadn't been a smoke detector, the fire wouldn't have been discovered and dealt with in time.

2 The child wouldn't have fallen in if there had been railings on that section of the river bank.

3 If Anthony had looked at the fuel gauge while he was driving, the car wouldn't have run out of petrol in the middle of the countryside.

4 There wouldn't have been such a huge outcry if the wood hadn't been destroyed in order to make way for the new motorway.

5 The disease wouldn't have spread rapidly if the health authorities had alerted people to the danger.

6 The pipe wouldn't have cracked last winter if the water had been disconnected.

7 The tomato plants would have withered if Robert hadn't ensured that they got plenty of fertiliser.

8 If most of the houses hadn't been specially constructed to withstand the shock, the earthquake would have caused a much greater amount/a great deal of damage.

9 Shirley wouldn't have phoned the service engineer to arrange a visit if the washing-machine hadn't been playing up.

10 Teresa wouldn't have got thin if she had eaten what was necessary to maintain her body weight.

D 1 The book wouldn't be wet if Sam hadn't left it on the grass.

2 Billy would be able to understand what Madame Maurice is saying if he had made an effort to keep up his French after he left school.

3 Sarah wouldn't be complaining about being sunburnt if she hadn't spent the whole afternoon lying in the sun.

4 Jane would be able to do her skirt up if she hadn't eaten so much on holiday.

5 The conservatory wouldn't be letting in water now if the builder had done a good job when he put it up.

6 The family wouldn't be heavily in debt if they hadn't been living beyond their means since they bought their new house.

7 I would be able to offer you some biscuits if the children hadn't eaten them all this morning.

8 The car wouldn't still be running smoothly if we hadn't had it serviced regularly.

9 The windows wouldn't look spotlessly clean if the window-cleaner hadn't come yesterday.

10 If I had brought a map, I wouldn't be lost.

Modals

A
1	Will	6	will; 'll
2	shall	7	'll; shall/will
3	'll	8	Shall
4	'll	9	'll; will
5	'll/will	10	'll/will/shall

B 1 ...., don't you think you should start learning Swedish?

2 '.......................... crisis?' 'I shouldn't think so.'

3 If I should die ...., this is what I should like ....

4 You shouldn't interrupt the boss at moments like this.

5 It was so kind of you to provide all this lovely food, but really, you shouldn't have.

6 We should forget about our problems ....

7 I shouldn't be at all surprised if Tim refused ....

8 Rachel shouldn't keep pestering her father ....

9 If I should be late, start the meeting without me.

10 Caroline shouldn't have tried to defraud the company she worked for.

C 1 May I sit here?

2 In the mountains, there may be an avalanche at any time.

3 Sam may be badly paid but he has ....

4 Jim may have had to stay behind at work.

5 Getting to the top may have been tough, but the view from the top was breathtaking.

6 May I speak to Mr Freeman please?

7 You may not remember me. I'm ....

8 There may be no one at home.

9 If you carry an introduction from Professor Mulligan, the librarian may let you in to see the manuscripts.

10 Of course, I may be mistaken but ....

D Group 1: 1,6,7 – reproach
Group 2: 2,4,5,10 – possibility
Group 3: 3,8,9 – concession

E 1 I needn't have taken any suntan lotion.

2 We didn't need to buy anything for breakfast the following day.

3 I needn't have left the house early.

4 We didn't need to take our own towels to the swimming-pool.

5 I didn't need to cut the grass on Saturday.

6 I didn't need to wait to see the doctor.

7 The candidate needn't have prepared such elaborate answers.

8 I didn't need to call the stewardess.

9 John needn't have been careful not to make a noise opening the door.

10 Harriet needn't have gone to such lengths to prepare a party.

F
opinion	2
challenge	4,11
annoyance	1
prohibition	5
fear	6,12
courage	3,7,8,9,10

G 1 Don't you dare take my bicycle./How dare you! Put that back.

2 I dare you to fight me.

3 I didn't dare ask my bank manager for another loan.

4 I dare say there will be a lot of snow this winter.

5 He dared to go into a cage with five lions in it.

6 I didn't dare tell him how cold it was.

7 I dare you to tell him.

8 How dare you say that it's not your fault!

9 Did you dare to ask the pianist about her interpretation?

10 I dare say John is a good worker, but he's not up to promotion.

Reported Speech

A 1 Michael said that the guests would be leaving at twelve o'clock.

2 The man on TV said that the special offer ended/would end on Saturday.

3 Gladys said that Mary was feeling a bit depressed.

4 The detective said that the Fraud Investigation team had discovered some disturbing information about Mr Fletcher's business activities.

5 The Chairman said that the committee would be discussing the plans for the new building.

6 The sergeant said that the patrol had rescued three men from the crashed helicopter.

7 Professor Challenger said that the survey team had been exploring the Mato Grosso for several weeks.

8 The production manager said that all the instruments had to/must be re-tested.

9 The registrar said that the information Mr Moriarty had asked for could not be provided.

10 The office manager said that all the furniture was going to be replaced.

B

1 The painter said that he wanted to finish the job that/the same day.
2 The foreman said that they would be able to start work at the beginning of the next/following week.
3 Janet said that she hadn't eaten since the day before.
4 Michael said that everything had been arranged on the morning of the day before/previous day.
5 The gardener said that everything would have been planted by the end of that year.
6 Jessica said that Steven was going to meet her there the next/following day.
7 The principal said that the interview had taken place that morning.
8 Mr Parkinson said that both his daughters were going to get married early in the next/following year.
9 Mr Moore said that the last total eclipse of the sun had been five years previously.
10 The customs officer said that it was essential that I paid the extra duty then.

C

1 Dr Fox asked Mrs Bell when she had started getting severe headaches.
2 The zoo-keeper asked how the animals had escaped from the cage.
3 The barrister asked why no safety checks had been carried out before take-off.
4 The Prince asked what had been done to help the homeless.
5 The journalists wanted to know which machine had done best in the tests.
6 Edmund wondered who would be the first to reach the summit.
7 Arnold asked if he needed to be a member to use the gym.
8 Harry asked who had won.
9 Jill asked Jack how his head was.
10 Mr Smart enquired if duty had to be paid on the goods.

D

1 Robin warned me that the mountains were full of bandits.
2 Rebecca reminded him about/to take his compass.
3 The courier informed the group that they would leave the hotel at seven a.m.
4 Frank congratulated me on winning first prize.
5 Elizabeth blamed me for our being late/the fact that we were late.
6 Bill told me that there was a fax for me.
7 The captain ordered the soldiers to carry the ammunition boxes to the forward positions.
8 Miranda thanked Alice for looking after the children.

9 Timothy promised his sister that he would be at the airport to meet her.
10 My secretary informed me that three of the interviewees had cancelled their appointments.

E

1 Sheila refused to accept the contract.
2 Nigel apologised for not finishing the report on time.
3 Nick admitted disposing of the bodies.
4 The chairman stated that profits had risen by twenty per cent that year.
5 The information officer explained that the delay had occurred because of a mechanical problem.
6 The salesman claimed that the new camera would be the best on the market.
7 Jeff denied taking part in the robbery.
8 Fiona suggested driving up to the Lakes.
9 The chairman added that turnover had increased by fifteen per cent.
10 The inspector reported that all the vehicles were in a satisfactory condition.

Sentence Synthesis

A   1 B   2 A   3 C   4 B   5 B

B

1 Holding the rifle firmly and taking aim, I pulled the trigger.
2 Trembling with fear and shivering with cold, Roland entered the tower.
3 Not having my keys, I couldn't start the car.
4 Without looking at me, he took the money.
5 On seeing the Pacific for the first time, he stood silent and amazed.
6 Feeling incredibly exhilarated, he pushed aside the stone that blocked the way to the Pharoah's tomb.
7 Finding no one at home, I immediately telephoned the police.
8 Tearing the secret letter into pieces and putting it into my mouth, I forced myself to swallow it.
9 Stretching out his arm, Michael wrenched the statue from its niche.
10 Not wanting to seem stupid, I said nothing at all.

C

1 Aged 30–40, ...
2 Educated to degree standard, ...
3 Holding a recognised qualification ....
4 Having joined our company, ...

5 Reporting to the Financial Director,

....

6 Based at our Basingstoke headquarters,

....

7 Working in a busy environment,

....

8 Employing over 2,000 staff,

....

9 Ranging from £30–40,000,

....

10 Given every opportunity for personal and professional development by our company, you and your

....

D
1 Samuel Browne, whom you met last week, will be visiting the office on Tuesday.
2 John Speke, who discovered the source of the Nile, was killed in a hunting accident.
3 (no commas needed)
4 (no commas needed)
5 I spoke to Her Royal Highness for two minutes, which was incredibly exciting.
6 (no commas needed)
7 (no commas needed)
8 This is my cousin, who will explain the system to you.
9 Martin had to visit the dentist again, which he hated.
10 The Duke of Wellington, whose socks he bid for at auction, is one of Richard's heroes.

E
1 He showed me two jackets, neither of which I liked.
2 He introduced me to three people, none of whom I had met before.
3 We saw three films, all of which I had seen before.
4 There were at least twenty people there, none of whom I knew.
5 Seven people applied for the job, some of whom were very well-qualified.
6 She offered me some orange-juice, a little of which I drank.
7 On the table were several oatcakes, a few of which I ate.
8 He gave me two books, both of which I had read before.
9 They delivered one hundred machines, none of which worked properly.
10 He has two sisters, both of whom are doctors.

F
1 Much as	6 in order to
2 However	7 as though
3 in case	8 to some extent
4 as long as	9 As soon as
5 Considering	10 Since

G
1 Whenever	6 anywhere
2 the same way	7 No matter
3 Everywhere	8 as if
4 for fear that	9 By the time
5 Seeing that	10 Directly

H
1 The dog doesn't eat children. 'Old English Sheepdog for sale. Especially fond of children. Will eat anything' would be better.
2 The phrase *skeleton staff* means there was only the minimum number of staff. It is an unfortunate expression in this context and would be better not used.
3 As it stands it means that the ladies are to stand in the sink. Change to: '. . . then stand them upside down in the sink.'
4 It should mean that the raid lasted four minutes, but it looks as if *minute* is an adjective describing the raiders. A hyphen in 'FOUR-MINUTE' would make it clear.
5 The exhibition in fact shows the work of the craftsmen, not the work of their rugs. Change the second sentence to: 'It features woven rugs by three British craftsmen.'
6 In the present sentence 'everyone' is a small college. This is impossible so start 'Since this is a small college, . . .
7 Start 'When he was a boy, . . .' to avoid the suggestion that his mother is a boy.
8 The phrase: 'in a plastic bag' appears to refer to 'a security man'. Move it to the position between 'found' and 'by'.
9 Put 'eating grass' after 'cow'. Here it is closer to 'he'.
10 The verb *shoplift* seems closely related to *weightlift* and suggests the champion is very strong! 'FOR STEALING FROM A SHOP' might be better in this example.

I
1 They cut down the trees, which had been there for sixty years, in order to sell the timber.
2 He returned to the village where he had been born and brought up but it had changed beyond recognition.
3 Although it was wet and muddy, he walked across the common because this would save him at least ten minutes.
4 Hans took a rope-ladder with him whenever he stayed in hotels, in case they caught fire.
5 Although he wore several pairs of socks it was so cold that he suffered frostbite in several toes.

6 As the weather has been extremely poor, the price of cabbages has doubled whereas the price of potatoes has remained steady because supplies have been imported from Egypt.

7 Although it made him feel sick he swallowed the fish's eye because he wanted to impress his friends.

8 He wrote a letter to Mr and Mrs Edwards, whose house he had stayed in for eight weeks while he gave a series of lectures, in order to thank them for their hospitality.

9 Even if they have extremely good qualifications, candidates will not be interviewed for this post unless they have at least five years' experience.

10 As he was short of money, he sold the painting which his grandfather, who had known the artist well, had given to him.

J
1 Eyestrain, leading to headaches and lack of concentration, may occur when the machine is used for long periods, but there are some precautions you can take that will reduce the problem.

2 It is important to avoid glare, which you can do by making sure that the brightness control is correctly adjusted and by positioning the screen so that there is no external reflection.

3 If you continue to feel uncomfortable after taking these precautions, you should fit special filters over the screen, which eliminate glare completely.

4 Accidental loss of material/information stored on disk could be catastrophic, so you should make copies of all disks, which you will need for everyday use.

5 Make sure the disk drive is empty before you switch on or off because sudden surges of power will damage disks/disks will be damaged by sudden surges of power.

6 Disks should be carefully labelled as soon as you have saved anything on them because you may assume that an unlabelled disk is blank and carelessly wipe out the valuable information on it/a disk containing valuable information.

7 The Pantheon, built in Rome on the orders of the Emperor Hadrian, is one of the finest Roman buildings and one which has inspired many later buildings.

8 In the fifth century, after attacking and capturing Rome, the Goths entered the Pantheon with the intention of destroying it/intending to destroy it, but the beauty of its interior stopped them in their tracks and it has survived to this day, its beauty relatively intact.

9 The tremendous public demand for our products, aided by extensive television coverage, has ensured that production is at an all-time high, as is the enthusiasm and dedication of staff.

10 It is hard to believe that it is only three years since we moved to our present site, which is one of the most advanced and productive factories in the U.K.

Adjectives, Adverbs and Inversion

A
1 a clever French girl
2 a beautiful medieval church
3 a long, blue, cotton skirt
4 an expensive new car
5 a large, well-preserved, medieval farmhouse
6 a small, white, porcelain figure
7 a very fine, Elizabethan, carved oak chair
8 the/some recent alarming news
9 an expensive, red silk Persian carpet
10 an ambitious young politician
11 an old, rather battered umbrella
12 a delightful, French country wine
13 a well-maintained, four-bedroomed, detached house
14 a delicious, hot, apple pie
15 a modern, wall-mounted, easy-to-dial telephone
16 a large, unbreakable, stainless steel flask
17 a tall, well-built, bearded man
18 a promising first novel
19 a thoroughly researched, well-written thesis
20 a long, clean, completely deserted beach

B

1 afloat		6	blazing
2 floating		7	alone
3 lone		8	sleeping
4 ablaze		9	live
5 alive		10	asleep

C

1 yet		6	still
2 yet		7	still
3 still		8	still
4 yet		9	yet
5 Still		10	still

D

1 quite/fairly		6	quite
2 rather		7	Quite; rather
3 fairly/quite		8	fairly; rather
4 rather		9	quite/fairly
5 rather		10	fairly/quite; rather

E
1 such
2 So
3 Such
4 so
5 Such; so
6 so
7 So
8 so
9 so
10 so

F
1 There weren't as many people at the committee meeting as the Chairman had expected.
2 Robert and Jilly don't see as much of their daughter as they would like to/their daughter as often as they would like.
3 The other members of the department are less well qualified than Joan/aren't as well qualified as Joan is.
4 Dan's car doesn't go nearly as fast as Frank's.
5 Jim didn't drink as much beer on Saturday night as he usually does.
6 Nowhere I have ever been is nicer than this.
7 Nothing I have heard is worse than this.
8 Britain is a much more densely populated country than Canada.
9 No one else behaved nearly as badly as Tom.
10 You can make as much fuss as you like, but you're not making me change my mind.

G
1 I wished to register my disapproval and also to bring about a change in policy.
2 Our team didn't manage to assert its superiority till the end of the match.
3 The captain allowed himself to celebrate his team's victory only when the last competitors had completed the course.
4 Thomas had not felt so carefree since his earliest years.
5 This runner's performance has been bettered only once.
6 The king was so displeased that he determined to rid himself of his advisors.
7 The composer was so enchanted with the beauty of the actress that he determined there and then that she was to be his wife.
8 Swans are seldom seen on this stretch of the river.
9 You'll only become a proficient pianist if you practise every day.
10 Simon had hardly completed a three-month overseas assignment before he was being pressed to take another.

H
1 Nowhere else will you find fossils like this.
2 In vain did he try to revive his comrade.
3 So strong were the hurricane winds that no building in the town escaped damage.
4 Only recently was the cause of cystic fibrosis discovered.
5 Harry is determined that never again will he be sent to prison.
6 Under no circumstances are friends and relatives seeing passengers off allowed into the departure lounge.
7 Not for one moment did I believe Jane's explanation.
8 Only when I heard the full story did I realise I had been taken in.
9 So great was their fear of the occupying army that few of the inhabitants were prepared to resist.
10 Only if you fall into one of the following categories will you be entitled to a reduction in the membership fee.

I
1 Only once did John break the rules but he suffered the consequences for the rest of his life.
2 Even after a second explanation the trainees still failed to understand the procedure.
3 In very few cases are the authorities prepared to allow exceptions to the rule.
4 No doubt Tim would have accepted the job if the salary package had been more attractive.
5 Even in the 1950's there was concern about potential damage to the environment.
6 Hardly ever does Sheila open her mouth at staff meetings.
7 On every occasion he was asked a question, the candidate's mind went blank.
8 In a few cases it was good to see that there was an astonishing response.
9 No longer was the office manager prepared to tolerate the level of absenteeism.
10 Only once will I repeat the information.

Prepositions

A
1 above
2 above
3 above
4 over
5 over
6 over; above
7 over
8 Above
9 over
10 above

B
1 below
2 below
3 under
4 under
5 beneath
6 below
7 beneath
8 Under
9 under
10 Beneath

C
1 as
2 as
3 like
4 Like; as; as
5 like
6 as
7 like
8 As; as
9 as
10 like

D
1 with
2 in
3 from
4 with
5 under
6 to
7 In
8 to
9 from
10 for

E
1 with; in
2 in
3 to
4 in
5 of
6 in
7 on
8 with
9 of
10 of; of

F
1 by
2 for; with; of
3 at
4 in
5 by
6 to
7 on
8 under
9 in
10 to; at

Vocabulary

A
1 alternate
2 alternative
3 all together
4 altogether
5 coast
6 shore
7 economical
8 Economic
9 disinterested
10 uninterested

B
1 migrate
2 memoirs
3 damage
4 industrial
5 agree
6 demonstration
7 household
8 intolerable
9 effective
10 conscious

C
1 delightful
2 bench
3 saving
4 embark
5 imagination
6 housework
7 female
8 deny
9 cloths
10 Actually

D
1 historical
2 prevent
3 creditable
4 definite
5 suite
6 habit
7 classical
8 convinced
9 treat
10 discover

E
1 stationary
2 imply
3 humane
4 exhaustive
5 aloud
6 effect
7 sensitive
8 notorious
9 besides
10 understandable

F
1 hopes
2 expect
3 expecting
4 expected
5 waiting for
6 expected
7 were expecting; hope; wait
8 wait
9 expects
10 expect

G
1 in the end
2 last but not least
3 latest
4 last
5 At the end
6 Eventually,
7 least
8 late; last
9 at last
10 at least

H
1 alive
2 live
3 living
4 life
5 Lives
6 life
7 living
8 live
9 Life
10 living

I
1 Decline
2 shattered
3 petered out
4 crumbled
5 decomposed
6 decayed
7 gone off
8 dispersed
9 dissolve
10 broke up

J
1 head
2 fist(s)
3 muscles
4 arms
5 knuckles
6 fingers
7 palm
8 nails
9 shoulders
10 feet
11 neck
12 lips
13 eyelashes
14 arms
15 toes
16 teeth
17 skin
18 hands
19 stomach
20 spine

K
1 sheep
2 guinea-pigs
3 whale
4 mammoth
5 rabbiting
6 dogged
7 hounded
8 catty
9 fishy
10 rat
11 pig
12 wolfed
13 elephant
14 Duck
15 wormed
16 sardines
17 waspish
18 beavering
19 stag
20 crows

L
1 sermon
2 maiden speech
3 soliloquy
4 jargon
5 debate
6 patter
7 dialect
8 speech impediment
9 commentary
10 inaugural address

M
1 stated
2 made
3 gave
4 says
5 dropped
6 raised
7 pays
8 swore; tell
9 make
10 recited

N
1 hit list
2 working party
3 night shift
4 quango
5 short list
6 task force
7 brigade
8 gang
9 Squad
10 Unit

O 1 A commercial art
     B a wet day
   2 A casual clothes
     B an unintelligent student
   3 A a patterned jumper
     B an attractive child
   4 A a tender steak
     B an easy job
   5 A a small helping
     B a mean woman
   6 A a hard winter
     B a strong cheese
   7 A a gentle slope
     B a reasonable/low price
   8 A a domestic animal
     B cultivated flowers
   9 A ill/poor health
     B bad behaviour
  10 A unfair treatment
     B dark hair
Note: not all possible alternatives are shown.

P 1 Would you like a biscuit or a sweet?
   2 Mr Carter's office is on the ground floor.
   3 She bought a dummy and some nappies
     for the baby.
   4 Take the lift to the top floor.
   5 We visited New England in the autumn.
   6 Jeff bought a waistcoat, a tie and some
     braces.
   7 Steve is very good at maths.
   8 He opened a current account at the bank.
   9 Robert asked his boss for a rise.
  10 Susan dived into the water.

Q 1 Lilian washed before dinner.
   2 He explained the government's defence
     policy.
   3 He wrote a cheque for new tyres.
   4 This ice-cream comes in sixty-five flavours.
   5 The theatre is in the centre of town.
   6 He used a megaphone to address the
     crowd.
   7 There was a jug of orange juice on the
     table.
   8 At the crossroads the sign said 'GIVE
     WAY'.
   9 He filled the bath with hot water.
  10 The new musical was a flop.

R 1 stew in his own juice
   2 splitting hairs
   3 skating on thin ice
   4 looking for a needle in a haystack
   5 sitting pretty
   6 putting a brave face on it
   7 touch and go
   8 he who pays the piper calls the tune
   9 egg on his face
  10 out of the frying-pan into the fire

S 1 get a word in edgeways
   2 quick on the uptake
   3 no need to rub it in
   4 caught . . . red-handed
   5 keep his hand in
   6 on the off chance
   7 talking to a brick wall
   8 keep a straight face
   9 right under your nose
  10 talk shop

T 1 kitty   6 perks
   2 snags   7 skives
   3 hang   8 nick
   4 plonk   9 eke out
   5 whip-round   10 come-uppance

U 1 dry run   6 spot checks
   2 crash course   7 dirt cheap
   3 powder keg   8 sandwich course
   4 cowboy   9 close shave
   5 ghost writer 10 hot potato

V 1 At the butcher's. English or New Zealand
     are types of lamb.
   2 At the garage. 'Four-star' means petrol.
   3 He bet some money on the 2.30 horse race
     at Newmarket racetrack.
   4 When buying washable clothes in strong,
     bright colours.
   5 Ordering paint or photographs which can
     have a dull or shiny finish.
   6 Two or more of the competitors finished
     the race at the same time.
   7 Your socks (for example) are being worn
     so that the inner surface is visible.
   8 At the dentist's. You are being invited to
     fill your mouth with antiseptic liquid and
     to spit it out at the end of treatment.
   9 The salary is too low for me to accept.
  10 Someone will appear on television.

W 1 hazards
   2 fossil fuels
   3 trend
   4 emissions
   5 greenhouse effect
   6 ozone layer
   7 global warming
   8 sea levels
   9 catastrophic
  10 local
  11 lead in petrol
  12 damage
  13 disposing of waste
  14 poured
  15 ecological balance
  16 inhibit
  17 acid rain

18 green movement
19 ecological dangers
20 fringe movement

X
1 stressful
2 pressure
3 traffic jams
4 rush-hour
5 congested
6 tube
7 mugged
8 picked
9 vandalism
10 graffiti
11 on the dole
12 redundancy
13 high-rise
14 inner-city
15 affluence

Y
1 achieve their potential
2 access
3 adapt their skills
4 national curriculum
5 primary education
6 secondary
7 tertiary
8 vocational education
9 training the mind
10 private education
11 entitled
12 funded
13 loan
14 drop-out
15 enter the labour market
16 skilled personnel
17 on-the-job
18 elite

Z
1 democracy
2 elections
3 express
4 universal suffrage
5 majority
6 cast their vote
7 secret ballot
8 goes to the polls
9 voter
10 ballot paper
11 polling booth
12 counted
13 constituency
14 proportional representation
15 minority groups
16 coalition
17 an overall majority
18 alliance

Phrasal Verbs

A
1 give anything away
2 gave off
3 give up
4 gave in
5 gives on to
6 give up
7 give them back
8 give up
9 gives out
19 giving up

B
1 putting it on
2 put off
3 put forward
4 put in for
5 put up with
6 put on
7 put you up
8 put out/off
9 put it about
10 put them off

C
1 do with
2 doing it up
3 do without
4 doing down
5 do away with
6 done out of
7 done in
8 do up
9 do with
10 done for

D
1 made out
2 make of
3 make up
4 making for
5 made off with
6 make out
7 making up
8 make it up
9 make out
10 make out

E
1 fell behind
2 falls to
3 fall out
4 fallen off
5 fall in
6 fell through
7 fell down
8 fell down
9 fell in
10 fell out

F
1 picked it up
2 picks on
3 picked at
4 pick up
5 pick out
6 picked up
7 pick off
8 pick up
9 picked up
10 pick out

G
1 take out
2 takes in
3 taken aback
4 take up
5 took it in
6 takes after
7 take-away
8 intake
9 taken down
10 takes it out

H
1 turns out
2 turn it down
3 turned away
4 turned out
5 turn on
6 turned up
7 turned on
8 turn to
9 turn down
10 turned up

I
1 Keep out
2 kept down
3 keep up
4 keeps it up
5 keeps to
6 keep up
7 keep on
8 keep in with
9 kept on
10 keep something back

J
1 Hold on
2 holds it against
3 held up
4 hold with
5 hold down
6 held out
7 held up
8 held off
9 hold out
10 hold back

K
1 clearing up
2 cleared away
3 cleared up
4 clear off
5 clear the matter up
6 clearing up
7 cleared out
8 cleared up
9 clearing it up
10 clear off

84

L
1. drop in
2. dropping off
3. drop out
4. drop the shopping in
5. drop out
6. dropped off
7. dropped back
8. dropped behind
9. dropped in
10. dropped off

M
1. stand for
2. stood around
3. stand in for
4. standing by
5. stand for
6. stands for
7. stand down
8. stand up for
9. stands out
10. stand up to

N
1. come round to
2. come about
3. come up
4. come out
5. come into
6. come round/to
7. Come off
8. come off
9. Come in
10. Come on

O
1. whisked away
2. warm-up
3. ease off
4. gone down with
5. brought down
6. phased out
7. bowled Tom over
8. crack down
9. soldier on
10. picked up

P
1. knocked out
2. clued up
3. run out of
4. fall-out
5. passed over
6. wear off
7. cooling off
8. pass up
9. called up
10. call-out

Q
1. take-off
2. turn-out
3. take-over
4. sell-out
5. getaway
6. shoot-out
7. stand-in
8. make-up
9. get-up
10. put-down

R
1. fed up
2. stand-by
3. tied up
4. put out
5. worn out
6. tired out
7. cut out for
8. over and done with
9. burnt out
10. done for

S
1. woke up
2. were pulled down
3. take off
4. took off
5. split up/broken up
6. laid off
7. took to
8. came round/to
9. took up
10. turned up at

Correct Verb Forms

A
1. has been typing; has not finished
2. have been getting; is; am
3. has just completed; wants; taking
4. has believed; has been trying; are
5. is thinking; has been wondering; would like; to accompany
6. has been spending; have been concentrating
7. looks; has been leaking; will have; is; to be put right
8. do not want; would prefer; can
9. Have you been to; have been wanting; has always come up; hope; to go; would like; to come
10. has given/is giving; shall have

B
1. looks; has lived; has worked; think; should definitely interview
2. was; fell; were brought down; have still not been fixed; were blocked; suffered; will be
3. still has not done so; shall have; to ask
4. had been complaining; was not surprised; left; will she do
5. have been trying; have you been
6. tried; look; will be able
7. have been questioning; have not got
8. is; is thinking; will wear/are going to wear
9. has breached; are now fleeing
10. is; have been; is

C
1. has Stephen telephoned; don't know; would stop; phoning
2. were; would you want to introduce
3. had not eaten; have made
4. would be; had allowed; is; will/shall have to start
5. agreed; kept
6. don't believe; said; has never lied/never lies
7. had realised; were coming; would have kept; is; am; is; come
8. offered; would you be
9. did you feel; received; was; would you not have been
10. is thinking of setting up; would you give

D
1. do you mean; was; has been; would not have called
2. had telephoned; invited; would you have done
3. would not have been; had not agreed
4. would not have got; had not spent; preparing
5. could speak/spoke; could; would have understood; we saw
6. would not have been overdrawn; had not written; to pay
7. is; is; were lying; enjoying; listening
8. agree; is; am not saying; is not; would co-operate
9. was going; received; had to stay; do not regret; have heard; went; was
10. regrets; being; is; would like; is not helping; being

E 1 did/would not keep playing; is; knowing; will work/is working
2 would taste; had added
3 were not raining; would be able
4 will not regret; spending; modernising; gets; sells
5 would have gone; had; did not want; turned out; came; should be admitted
6 said; she would be; have missed; hope; won't; will be;
7 will you do/are you going to do; finishes/has finished; don't know; will have; look
8 would not be asking; did not feel
9 will you do; gave; I'll just say; was mistaken
10 reads/has read; will be; had left

F 1 asks; have gone; will be; can; needn't worry; won't be
2 steps; will be greeted; will be driven; will take place; is; will be taken; will spend
3 would have told; was; made
4 didn't realise; had passed; had known; would not have insisted

5 realised; did not understand/had not understood; repeated
6 Had it not been; would not have been able; was; managed; am
7 closed; had been teaching there; decided; is
8 took place; were accepted
9 has become
10 rocked; were seen; forced to resign

G 1 have been; heard; had won; did you do
2 have been trying; to get; have gone; Have you; will be
3 didn't need; to tell; had already heard; had told
4 to have let; could; had; needn't have got
5 have given; shouldn't have done
6 did not dare; wanted; was
7 has been offered; isn't able to decide; should take; has; to let; know
8 spent; making; needn't have bothered; rang; to say; wasn't able to come
9 Are; is; should be; isn't; have forgotten; to include
10 had; dare not